Anvil of the Gods

AIRMEN & AIRCRAFT
Martin Caidin, General Editor

Also:

HERITAGE OF VALOR, by Colonel Budd J. Peaslee, USAF Retired

TRACKS ACROSS THE SKY, by Page Shamburger

THE SILKEN ANGELS, by Martin Caidin

Modern Airplanes
versus
Violent Storms

ANVIL
OF THE
GODS

by Fred McClement

J. B. LIPPINCOTT COMPANY

Philadelphia and New York

*To my son, Roy—who, had he lived
beyond his seventeen years, would have been
a wonderful pilot*

Foreword

Anvil of the Gods is a book worth publishing by any standards because of the skill of its author both as a capable reporter and as a writer. But there is a much greater meaning to this book, and because it is possible that some will misinterpret its message, this brief foreword is necessary.

Some readers will draw the erroneous conclusion that this book capitalizes on the crashes and destruction of a number of great airliners, and that it takes advantage of the obviously important meaning to airline passengers. Nothing of the sort is intended.

Yet there can be no escaping the grim fact that many airliners have met disaster in the sky, and have become the catastrophes splashed across newspaper front pages. We cannot avoid these facts—simply because they *are* facts.

Airliners, despite the most rigid safety requirements, have been on too many occasions hurled from the sky. Some of them have been literally torn apart in midair; others have plummeted out of control. These things have happened where the crew met every requirement, and more; where the airplane met and exceeded the structural and safety requirements demanded not only by the United States Government but also by its builder and the airline.

The trap in the sky is the storm—storms with energy beyond

our comprehension, storms with forces so violent that only recently have we begun to understand their nature.

Consider that in this modern age of flight with the world's finest aircraft, the finest sources of power, the highest crew standards, a great radar network, a vast electronic network for navigation and communications, a huge amount of meteorological reporting and forecasting, and an enriched scientific understanding of storms—that, despite all these factors, in the period from February 1963 to February 1964 some 558 human beings perished in ten airline tragedies resulting directly from violent storms.

It is the contention of the author that the fault has been our lack of understanding of the violence in the skies. Mr. McClement has stated that "if this study of the power of storms and their lethal effects on aircraft will create improved weather forecasting, a clearer understanding of the violence to which planes have been subjected, and if it will result in new studies, more caution in plunging headlong into storms—then this book will have been more than worthwhile." With this I am in full agreement. Because a clearer understanding of the violence contained within the storms will bring men to avoid that violence, and such evasion will save lives.

That is the purpose of this book.

Anvil of the Gods does not present conclusions, nor does it find a panacea to the serious problem. Solutions still lie in the hands of the engineers and in the wisdom of those pilots who avoid storms—and survive. This book concerns itself only with facts.

MARTIN CAIDIN

Preface

On August 31, 1940, a Pennsylvania Central Airlines DC-3 was flying through a severe electrical storm when a flash of lightning erupted directly in front of the plane. It nosed over and dived into the ground near Lovettsville, Virginia, carrying twenty-four persons to their deaths.

At that time, it seemed incomprehensible that a modern airliner could be affected in such a frightening manner by a mere thunderstorm, and the investigation of the disaster by the Civil Aeronautics Board was most thorough. The U. S. Bureau of Standards, the airframe manufacturer, and the engine maker were brought together to conduct an intensive probe into the crash. The Federal Bureau of Investigation seized an alarm clock but could find no evidence that it had triggered a blast. Finally, after months and months of painstaking research, the result of the first fatal-crash investigation by the CAB found that, indeed, it had been caused by a thunderstorm.

From that day onward, thunderstorms took their place as possible causes of air disasters. But how much have we learned in the interim?

From the Lovettsville episode through the end of the war, there were two more passenger plane crashes caused by thunderstorms and these took forty-four persons to their deaths.

From 1945, at the end of the war, until 1959, there were eight air disasters attributed to storms, with a death toll of 270 persons—all in the continental United States. Three more were recorded in other parts of the world.

Then there was a lull and the jets came into action.

In 1963, there were eight storm disasters with modern air transports which took 301 lives and injured 66 persons. Three of the crashes involved U. S. flag lines and caused a loss of 151 lives.

Obviously, something is wrong. I have not attempted to solve the problem in these pages, but have presented the facts so that others may study them and act accordingly.

Without the co-operation and assistance of the following agencies and organizations this book would not have been possible:

The Civil Aeronautics Board, Federal Aviation Agency, United States Weather Bureau, United States Air Force, Royal Canadian Air Force, the British Ministry of Aviation, the Canadian Department of Transport, as well as the flag lines of the United States, Air Canada, and the Air Lines Pilots Association.

Thanks are also due a large number of pilots, newspaper reporters, and photographers who were involved, in one way or another, in the events described in this book.

F. McC.

Bloomfield Hills, Mich.
March, 1964

Contents

How strange the soft white billowy clouds of summer
cause such torment in the skies,
Refresh the land and breathe new life and vigor to the air,
Decorating the sunsets with the gaudy magnificence of untamed
power brilliant, beautiful and dangerous,
Recharged by the chemistry of space into glittering fairyland castles
That mask the awful powers beneath the towering Anvil of the Gods,
Where Nature has frolicked since the dawn of time
unhindered to eternity.

Birds Don't Fly in Thunderstorms

1

ON CLEAR AFTERNOONS, from the fields near Issoudun one can see the incomparable grandeur of Quebec city over ten miles away. The bold headland of Cape Diamond rises for hundreds of feet above the St. Lawrence River and is crowned by the battlements of the Citadel that have withstood the ravages of war and time. Above the thin gray line of the upper walls and almost imperceptible except in the rays of the late afternoon sun the unchanging panorama of steeples and the imposing sentinel of the Château Frontenac etch themselves upon the pastel blue skies beyond.

Here is history, silent and omnipresent, basking peacefully above the famous river which introduced the white man to the rich uncharted interior of a vast new land. Here the French and English tried to control a continent, and on these ramparts fought a decisive battle.

To French-Canadian Brutel Seurremen it was a delightful vista which his pale blue eyes seldom tired of watching. He was not concerned with history. His daily life was dedicated to the rich black soil, which he worked with his hoe. When he became fatigued in his labor, he would rest on his hoe handle, mop his perspiring brow with an earth-stained red bandanna, and gaze northeastward across the dozen miles of carefully nurtured flatlands that separated him from Quebec city.

The sun shone warm and generously. A slight east wind stirred the golden wheat in the fields. It was a scene of pastoral serenity, silent and inspiring, and Brutel loved its unchanging simplicity. In the nearby village of Issoudun, the church bell tolled the hour.

It was 2 P.M.

Brutel shifted his weight and again wiped his brow. The air was hot and humid. Presently the wind increased, whipping the dry topsoil into miniature whirlwinds. A clap of thunder startled Brutel and he turned to see a thunderstorm bearing down on the village from the west. Black and ominous, lightning of savage intensity flashed in its midst, creating a constant electrical cannonade. Close to the ground, scud clouds swirled and eddied immediately ahead of the black sweeps of rain.

The storm made its way ponderously across the landscape. Brutel guessed it would pass south of the farm. Suddenly, a bolt of lightning stabbed the ground not more than half a mile from where he stood, and Brutel decided to head for the farmhouse and await the storm's passing. He picked up his hoe in his right hand, balanced it, took a parting look at the distant city and turned to leave.

A glint of silver caught his eye. He looked northeastward again: there he saw an airliner winging its way in his direction. It droned steadily onward, defying the storm in its path, mocking the even tenor of the world below. His gaze followed the airliner for a minute or so. Brutel often paused to look up at the great airplanes passing over his countryside en route to Montreal from the far-off lands of Europe. Sometimes they appeared two or three times a day. Although he had never flown in a plane and guessed he never would, Brutel liked to watch them just as he liked to watch the hawks wheel and dive over the meadows.

Brutel watched the giant silver airliner head directly into the magnificent white clouds that marked the leading edge of the storm. As the swirling vapors closed around the plane, he started for the farmhouse. He moved a few steps and then stopped suddenly, startled and frightened by a strange and horrifying sound. The sound came from within the storm clouds. It was like sheets of tin being banged back and forth against trees.

Bang, bang, bang. The noise intensified, becoming more terrible by the second. And then the earth shook from a tremendous explosion. It momentarily deafened Brutel. It rocked him off his feet and he collapsed to his knees in the soft earth. He shivered with fright until the soft cool rain brought him to his senses. Abandoning his hoe, he ran in the direction of the swamp at the south end of his farm, toward the vicinity of the explosion.

In the village of Issoudun the parish priest, the Rev. Alexander Deblois, had paused in his walk along the main street to watch the airliner and to contemplate the approaching storm. He saw it enter the clouds, and heard the tremendous explosion a few seconds later. Immediately surmising that the explosion came from the aircraft, he ran to the fire hall. Further up the street, Andre LeClerc had slumped to the ground from the concussion of the blast. When he finally shook the dizziness from his head, he scrambled to his feet and headed out of the village in the direction of the swamp. Five nuns, defying the mounting wind and the threat of rain, joined LeClerc and ran across the fields to lend their assistance.

Other villagers raced from their duties and arrived at the spongy muskeg only to recoil in horror. Scattered over the still smoking bog were fragments of human beings: arms, legs, heads—mixed together with scraps of aluminum, clothing, luggage, papers, and souvenirs of Europe.

The people of Issoudun stood silent before the ghastly scene. Father Deblois fell to his knees and recited the last rites over the scattered remains. The thick black mud of the Quebec swamp was now the temporary grave of that giant silver airliner and the seventy-nine men, women and children it had carried. The villagers, standing with their heads bowed in prayer beneath the fury of the storm, did not realize they were witnesses to the worst disaster in Canadian aviation history, up to that time.

At Malton Airport in Toronto, Ontario, hundreds of friends and relatives of the passengers—for this was a special flight from London to Toronto—had arrived to give them a rousing homecoming. Newsmen and photographers mixed with the crowd to begin the long wait which would provide them with a story vastly different from what they expected.

The Maritime Central Airways' DC-4 had taken off from London's Heathrow Airport overloaded. Only the fact that it was a dependable DC-4 explains how it became airborne for the long flight home.

The DC-4 was a long-range transport that helped world-wide aviation come of age. Built by Douglas Aircraft of Santa Monica, the same people who created the great DC-3, it was an aircraft that helped to change man's concepts of speed and distances. With its four powerful engines it would carry 32,000 pounds in its cavernous interior and fly nonstop for more than 3,000 miles. It was designed to tame the long inhospitable stretches of the North Atlantic and firmly establish intercontinental trade and travel, not only for the United States but for other countries as well.

The Douglas DC-4 was born the C-54 in 1939. Before the last plane was delivered in August 1947, many changes were made by the manufacturer to cope with new and more powerful engines and with the transition from military versions to the commercial versions. The C-54A was a triple-tailed aircraft, but this configuration was changed at the beginning of the war to the C-54B, with a single tail, a range of 3,100 miles, 49 seats, and an all-up weight of 52,000 pounds. The Maritime Central aircraft was a C-54B built in 1944, with 1,450 horsepower engines (take-off). Its maximum cruise speed was 265 miles an hour, while its cruising speed was established at 235 miles an hour, according to load and height.

The C-54C was in mock-up only, and the next design to fly was the C-54D with 48 seats, and this was followed by the first commercial version, the C-54E, with 44 seats which were gradually increased. It was this model that became the first DC-4, and all C-54's were changed to the new name. There was an "F" model (only one), and several "G" models which had a

Perhaps the greatest airplane ever built, the DC-3 provided safety and reliability to the budding air transportation industry. One airline bought forty-eight of these planes, retiring the last one in 1963, and never lost a single plane. (American Airlines photo)

Douglas Aircraft, builder of the DC-4, called the plane "Skymaster." These planes survived many a stormy flight. (American Airlines photo)

range of 4,000 miles. The DC-4 was 27 feet 6 inches in height . . . 93 feet 10 inches in length with a wingspan of 117 feet 6 inches.

From the first C-54 to the last DC-4, Douglas built a total of 1,242 planes, of which 79 were made specifically for commercial use. In 1945, American Airlines had eight DC-4's in use, Pan American nineteen, TransWorld eighteen, and Air France one.

From an original 49 seats, the newer versions climbed to 80 seats, but some operators jammed as many as 100 tourists in some of them. The last models had a gross weight of 69,500 pounds although the military overload on the plane was as high as 82,500 pounds.

When hostilities ceased, there was a rush to purchase the military versions to convert them for passenger service. During the few years between the end of World War II and the introduction of the superlative DC-6, the scheduled airlines of the U. S. were operating 579 converted DC-4's on domestic routes and 127 on foreign routes. While they were fighting for new routes and better fare structures, the unscheduled airlines fought them for business.

By flouting a number of the laws of physics and mathematics, many unscheduled operators squeezed more seats into the DC-4, often totaling as many as 90 or 100 seats on some runs. Competitively, they became a force to be reckoned with by the regular carriers. From the end of the war to the beginning of the '50's, the unscheduled operators pressed 2,700 transports of all kinds into service. Even after the introduction of the high-speed *Constellations* and the long-range *Stratocruisers*, the old DC-4 was still handling much of the lucrative transatlantic business, flying excursion groups to Europe at cut-rate fares.

The big airlines were being hard pressed. American Airlines, North Atlantic pioneer, dropped its overseas operations in 1949 to concentrate on the domestic runs, leaving the European trade to the non-skeds and the government-owned European airlines. For travelers who didn't mind the overcrowding and sometimes marginal observance of safety rules, who didn't care for a full-course meal with champagne, and who could bear the

The DC-6, with its longer range, quieter and more powerful engines, and luxurious appointments, carried on the tradition of dependability established by the DC-3. In turbulence it behaved exceptionally well. (American Airlines photo)

pressure of passengers squeezed in on either side, the non-skeds offered economy. However, those non-skeds still operating have generally brought themselves into line with the regulations governing air safety.

One of the many Atlantic non-sked operators at the time was Maritime Central Airways, of Moncton, New Brunswick. This organization operated a fleet of transports in eastern Canada, concentrating on the nerve-wracking business of supplying men and materials to the inhospitable wilderness of Labrador where vast iron ore reserves were being exploited. It also operated carriers to Newfoundland, the North Shore of the St. Lawrence, and to communities in eastern Canada. Some of its flights were scheduled. Maritime Central also entered the North Atlantic competition with low-rate chartered flights to the British Isles.

One of the DC-4's of the North Atlantic run, owned and operated by Maritime Central, stood on the black macadam parking ramp of London's Heathrow Airport on Saturday, August 10, 1957. The rain that had fallen in the forenoon had left its weather-beaten skin gleaming in the midafternoon sun. Looking sadly out of place in the long line of *Super Constellations, Viscounts, Comets* and other newer aircraft, this first flagship of the North Atlantic was the scene of intense activity as fuel trucks loaded its wings with high-octane gasoline and ground crewmen piled hundreds of traveling bags and cases into its cavernous hold.

At 5 P.M., one of the many green buses of Heathrow dashed from the airport operations center to the DC-4. Out of it stepped the crew who would guide the plane on its impending flight across the North Atlantic. The flight plan would follow the great circle route from London to Toronto, with a refueling stop at Keflavik, Iceland, and another at Montreal. Captain Norman Ramsay, of Toronto, walked around the aircraft, giving it his traditional visual check. His first officer, Paul Renaud, of Montreal, immediately boarded the aircraft to prepare it for the long flight, a job which he had performed routinely on many occasions. He was followed by Gordon Stewart, also a first officer and also of Montreal. Lou Morgan, the navigator, struggled up the boarding ramp, his heavy brief case bulging with maps, navigation papers, and instruments. Morgan came from Australia and only recently had joined Maritime Central.

Two pretty stewardesses, Anne Harvey and M. C. LeBlanc, both of Moncton, New Brunswick, were last up the ramp and began their duties of activating the hot beverage tanks, packing several cases of sandwiches into the cold cabinets, and checking seats, cushions and blankets.

At 5:35 P.M., two other green buses disgorged their loads at the ramp, and seventy-one adults and two children marched aboard; a total of seventy-three passengers on an aircraft originally designed for forty-nine. Incidentally, there were fourteen married couples in the group.

They all looked tired, having spent the last month tramping the European battlefields, for all the men were former members of the Canadian contingent of the famous British Expeditionary Force in France, who in World War I had earned the name of "Old Contemptibles." They had revisited the even fields of Flanders where the poppies still grew in profusion, the farm lands of Passchendaele once rich with mud and lice, Cambrai with its broken stone walls, and Vimy Ridge, the scene of one of Canada's great military glories.

Now exhausted, their minds rich with memories, their arms loaded with souvenirs of a trip that would never be repeated, they took their seats in the DC-4 and settled back for the long trip home.

Typical of the vets was James Pinkney, sixty-eight years old, of Toronto. He had lost his wife the year before and, fearing that his own span was ebbing to a close, had eagerly signed up for the return to France and Belgium. Partly crippled by wounds, coughing from the aftereffects of poison gas, Pinkney had often remarked, "I must see Cambrai again, somehow I must. . . . I must."

The opportunity of a low-cost tour had appealed to him as to the other vets, and he had saved his meager earnings as an apartment janitor in order to make the pilgrimage. Now he slumped back in his aircraft seat, his mind content with the memories of his youth.

In the doorway, an agent checked his watch. It was five forty-five o'clock. He withdrew the ramp and the last of the green buses scurried away. Capt. Ramsay brought the four Pratt & Whitneys to life and the blast from the swirling propellers rippled the rain puddles on the black surface. The DC-4 eased into the perimeter aisle and rumbled to the runway at the eastern end of the vast airport. Half a mile to the south, the tower crew saw the Maritime Central plane, acknowledged Ramsay's request for his air traffic routing, and cleared the giant ship for its take-off.

At 5:55 P.M., the DC-4 roared down the Heathrow runway and groaned along almost 5,000 feet before divorcing itself from the concrete, its four propellers chewing on the air to sustain its life. The passengers sighed with relief. The flight was airborne.

The plane climbed slowly for several minutes and then turned right over the Thames River and leveled out, permitting the passengers on the left side to see the imposing panorama of Windsor Castle below and the sprawling buildings of Cambridge University a short distance beyond the silvery river. In the gathering light, Liverpool shone like an industrial diamond, Manchester glowed behind a cloak of smog, and by the time the flight had reached the airlane west of Glasgow, the night was on all sides and the stars shone blue-white and cold.

The blinking green beacon at Prestwick Airport disappeared rearward from the right side, the blue high-intensity lights of Troon melted into the darkness, and Glasgow, a wide saucer of brilliance, glowed and sparkled until the aircraft had passed beyond the Grampian Mountains on its course toward the inhospitable Hebrides. From here on, only the occasional light on the Scottish islands broke the blackness of the night below. Droning onward while the passengers slept, the chartered flight left the Hebrides behind and headed toward Iceland, 550 miles to the northwest, across the cold and angry North Atlantic Ocean.

It was now 9 P.M., and the plane was halfway to its first stop. The flight to Iceland was quiet and uneventful and at midnight the distant lights of Reykjavik came into view and the crew gently lowered the aircraft at 500 feet per minute, crossing southeast of the Icelandic capital to execute a landing across the bay at the airport of Keflavik. The DC-4 refueled while the passengers rushed to the terminal to send postcards to friends and relatives in Canada and the United States. It was a long way from nowhere, the food was excellent and inexpensive, and the stamps were pretty.

The Keflavik forecaster had good news for Ramsay and his crew. The weather was clear all the way to Montreal. There would be no sweating on this trip, other than getting the overloaded plane off the ground. The passengers reboarded the aircraft at 12:55 A.M., and the DC-4 lumbered down the southwest runway a few minutes later, airborne over the boundary lights at exactly 1:12 A.M. The next stop would be Montreal, unless the strength of the headwinds necessitated an unscheduled fuel stop at Quebec city. Ramsay expected to reach Montreal in about nine hours. His course would follow a straight line from Iceland to Cape Farewell, on the southernmost tip of Greenland, and then a slight deviation to the left to Goose Bay, on Hamilton Inlet on the Labrador coast. After a check with Goose Bay, the plane would continue over the Labrador and Quebec wilderness to Seven Islands off the north shore of the St. Lawrence River. It would then change course slightly to the west to pass over Mont Joli on the south side of the river, over Quebec city at the narrows of the great stream, and thereafter begin the descent to Montreal.

The DC-4 droned southwestward over the utter loneliness of the berg-choked ocean 8,000 feet below. Activity in the cockpit never ceased as the navigator plotted the pressure systems of the North Atlantic while the pilots kept up a continuous chatter with the lightships and shore stations and experimented with fuel mixtures to give the best fuel consumption for the 2,400-mile hop to the next stop. Star fixes and long-range radio signals set the course for the seemingly uneventful flight.

The Maritime Central crew at this moment had already been

on duty for some twenty hours and flying almost constantly for fifteen or sixteen hours. They had flown eastward across the Atlantic to pick up the charter passengers and had taken only enough time in London to refuel for the long journey back to Canada. Their fatigue may account for the appalling events which were soon to occur.

Death was stalking the DC-4.

Dawn disclosed the ocean whitecaps far below, faint specks of white on a turbulent sea of gray-green, laced at intervals with white castles of icebergs. By midmorning the low, uninviting Labrador coast came into view and the long silvery arm of Hamilton Inlet lay dead ahead. Over the airport at Goose Bay, Capt. Ramsay reported his position, reset his altimeter, listened to the latest weather reports for eastern Canada and the Gulf of St. Lawrence, and continued on over the rocky wilderness toward Seven Islands. The passengers were having coffee and sweet rolls. The air was smooth and unclouded and the passengers appeared grateful. They moved about to stretch their legs and chatted about the events of the past thirty days.

Had they known they were flying with Captain Norman Ramsay, the former Trans-Canada Air Lines pilot who had been dismissed recently for negligence and lack of alertness in the cockpit, they might have had some serious second thoughts about their chances of a safe and sound arrival in Montreal and Toronto.

Ramsay was a strange, moody, autocratic man; handsome in uniform, quick to make friends, just as quick to dissolve his friendships. A veteran pilot of TCA he had been at the controls of an inaugural *Super Constellation* flight from Tampa, Florida, to Toronto's Malton Airport on the night of December 17, 1954, when his "judgment" could have cost the lives of some forty passengers had it not been for a miraculous piece of luck.

The aircraft involved was brand-new. It was the pride of the TCA fleet, which had been relying for many years on older, noisier 40-passenger planes. The *Super Connie* was the answer to the company's intense transatlantic competition with a score of other famous airlines. The sixty-six passenger *Super Constel-*

lation could be switched off the Atlantic runs during the winter and placed on the lucrative hops to Florida. The Tampa-Toronto flight, with Ramsay at the controls, was the first of the Florida runs. It was an historic occasion.

When the giant aircraft raised Toronto from the southwest, Ramsay received his landing instructions from the Malton Approach Control. He maneuvered the throbbing *Connie* eastward over Toronto, turned north to parallel the airport runway which he would use when he swung south for the landing. Low scud clouds and high overcast did not obscure the airport. As the pilot of a *Viscount* from New York flying right behind Ramsay later said: "It stood out like a sore thumb."

Northeast of Malton, Ramsay banked westward and then south, to line up his aircraft with the runway. He was five miles from the touchdown. Over the outer marker, a radio guideline to the airport, Ramsay's co-pilot jumped up in his seat from surprise. The aircraft was some 400 feet under the minimum for this area.

Most pilots would have reacted instantly to such a situation by immediately applying more power to the aircraft and lifting the nose to gain back the lost height. Ramsay did not. He curtly told his first officer to mind his own business and to concern himself with the duties of putting the wheels down and controlling the flaps on the wings to slow down the giant plane when the high forward speed was no longer required.

Suddenly the *Connie* shuddered. It shook like a crazy thing. Passengers were thrown forward at their seats. The giant plane had collided with a tree and some of the branches were protruding from the leading edge of the wing.

Another thump, this one more violent. The lights went out. Passengers screamed. Before they knew what was happening, the aircraft split open like a ripe melon, spewing the passengers, still strapped in their seats, all over the farm field into which it had landed. Giant Curtiss-Wright turbocompound engines bounced like corks along the ground and small fires began to lick at torn fuel cells.

Ramsay had flown the aircraft into the ground, three miles

short of the runway. He sustained injuries and so did his crew. But miraculously not one of the passengers was killed or seriously injured. All of them released their seat belts and ran or crawled across the snowy, icy ground to put as much distance as they could between themselves and the fires around the scattered wreckage.

Following this accident, and incidentally the writing off of a brand-new multimillion-dollar aircraft, Ramsay spent several weeks in the hospital recovering from shock. Investigation by TCA revealed his behavior to have been negligent and that he had lacked alertness while at the controls. He was fired.

In his own defense, Capt. Ramsay pointed out he had been at the controls for many hours before the crash and was fatigued. Government and company investigators did not agree that this defense was sufficient to cause such negligence and he lost his license to fly for six months.

A mounting wave of public sympathy for Ramsay began to make itself felt in the press and in public discussions. Here was a long-time pilot and a senior captain on Canada's own public airline. He was now like a doctor without instruments, a craftsman without tools, a man deprived of his livelihood because of one accident, the only one in his life, and no one was killed. You could always buy a new airplane. Many pilots thought that Ramsay had enough punishment in losing his license for six months without being fired from his job.

But what the pilots didn't know and what the public didn't know was that Norman Ramsay was a sick man, a pilot whose judgment could be warped by fatigue, a flier disturbed by heights and particularly disturbed during level changes when his flying judgment often left him entirely.

No one knew of these symptoms except Ramsay and his doctor and only calamity would reveal them.

Certainly his fellow crew members and his passengers never knew that his judgment would become so disorientated during long hours of flying as it did on this pleasant morning of August 11, 1957. Only the crew on the flight deck knew that he was the same Ramsay who had crashed the TCA airliner two years before and who had joined Maritime Central Airways when his pilot's license had been returned to him. Once a pilot gets back his license, he has a clean bill of health and can be hired by any airline.

The crew radioed their position over Seven Islands and Mont Joli. The aircraft was now approaching Quebec city, visible at the narrows of the river with the long steel-arched bridge just beyond.

Should Ramsay land at Quebec and refuel? Most pilots would have done so. There were only approximately 122 gallons left in the fuel tanks—barely sufficient to reach Montreal, but enough if the plane's path did not deviate and traffic patterns did not hold it up.

Ramsay elected to continue on to Montreal. Perhaps his old enemy fatigue warped his judgment. But he was in absolute command of the flight deck. He was on course and on time. He kept going.

At 2:07 P.M., the flight reported to radio operator Raoul Roy, at Quebec city's Ancienne Lorette Airport: "Over the Quebec range at 6,000 feet, estimating Montreal at 3:07 P.M. . . . Over and out."

Operator Roy jotted the communication in his log. It was the last word from the flight. Twenty minutes later, Roy knew he should hear from the flight again as it crossed over a compulsory check point between Quebec and Montreal. But no radio contact broke the silence. Roy noted the failure in his log and then reported the breach to Air Traffic Control, who, in turn, attempted to contact the flight without success, though the heavy static being discharged from a tremendous thunderstorm some distance to the southwest of Quebec city might have garbled the signals.

Ramsay continued on course after crossing the Quebec radio range. The storm blocked the skyway ahead of him, maybe twelve to fifteen miles. It seemed unusually high and wide and the plane had not sufficient fuel to circumnavigate it. Ramsay elected to go through. The FASTEN YOUR SEAT BELTS lights would have been activated in the passenger cabin and the speed of the airliner probably would have been reduced as it entered the strange caverns of clouds, white on the outside, gray and black in the center.

The airliner began to yaw and shake sharply and sickeningly. Torrential rain enveloped it. The day became black. Tremendous updrafts of air lifted the airliner upward. Downdrafts shook it violently. The plane pitched and yawed, attempting to shake the storm's grip. The crew was unable to control the bucking, climbing and diving. The DC-4 nosed over, pointed straight down and roared earthward at a frightening rate of speed. It was utterly out of control.

Mercifully the passengers had only seconds in which to contemplate their fate. The Maritime Central charter slammed into the swampland near Issoudun with a roar like thunder and a percussive explosion. The DC-4 folded like an eggshell while its engines churned their way below the sodden surface of the ground. The only sound now was the patter of raindrops and the hissing of hot metal. Thunder rumbled a requiem from the cloud castles above.

It took time for the citizens of Issoudun to contact the authorities in Quebec city. At first it was difficult to get a call over the busy lines of this rural area. Then came the frustrating explanations to distant officials in the long chain of responsibility leading to the people who should be concerned with such a disaster. It was not until 6:30 P.M. that the Royal Canadian Air Force reported the observance of wreckage near Issoudun. One hour later, three parachutists dropped to the scene with first-aid equipment and medicines.

The first thing the chutists saw at the smoldering swamp was the horrible sight of an infant child, seemingly unharmed, seated in the pilot's seat, some considerable distance from the main crash scene. Continuing their investigation, the three-man team found an undamaged propeller 2,000 feet from the main impact area. Other small bits of metal and human remains lay scattered over a half-mile area.

The largest piece of wreckage found was a slice of tail, twelve inches wide and seven feet long. The scene of the main impact

The interior of a cumulo-nimbus cloud is black as night. This spectacular photograph, taken from the cockpit of a plane flying beneath the base of the storm, shows the heavy rain showers ahead. (Photo by James Yarnell)

was now a crater of green water with bits of shiny metal showing through. The paratroopers repaired to the village to arrange for the protection of the scene for the investigation which would follow. Unfortunately, the authorities seemed to move much too slowly.

Before the Department of Transport crash investigators arrived the next day, curious sightseers had flocked from Quebec and other nearby cities and towns, moving amid the wreckage, grabbing at souvenirs, carrying away bits and pieces of the personal possessions of the dead passengers. By the time the government moved, souvenir hunters had carried away thousands of small parts of the aircraft, parts that might have been necessary for the investigation of the crash. It took searchers three days and nights to reach the main wreckage and it took them many weeks to piece together the pitiful fragments.

Only twenty bodies could be identified. The rest were churned to unrecognizable pulp and were shoveled into six boxes. Pens and pencils, which normally remain intact after even the worst air crashes, were smashed to bits in this one. Pearls were pulverized into powder. Jewels were split into fragments. It took probers four more days of digging with earth movers and steam shovels to reach the engines, *an unbelievable eighty-six feet below the surface.*

As is usual following air disasters, a public board of enquiry was set up to hear witnesses and to attempt to establish the cause of the accident. Just before this hearing officially got under way, Queen Elizabeth, from her castle at Balmoral, Scotland, sent to the Canadian Government a note of condolence for the men who had once served her grandfather and her Empire so illustriously, and her sympathy to those who survived.

One of the witnesses to testify at the inquiry was Lieut. Georges Lacroix, twenty-one-year-old pilot with the Royal Canadian Navy. He told of flying over Issoudun that afternoon, at almost the same time as the Maritime Central DC-4. He had first encountered the thunderstorm with its giant anvil cloud about twenty-five miles southwest of Quebec city. He was flying a *Harvard* training aircraft.

Deciding that he could safely fly under the storm, he had entered the churning scud clouds at a low altitude and for a moment wondered what had happened. He had never encountered a like situation, probably because he was a novice pilot. His *Harvard* was picked up like a toy and tossed about like a cork on a stormy sea. His altimeter moved crazily as the aircraft alternately shot upward and dashed downward in the grip of the air currents.

Lacroix testified that finally he had brought the plane under control after plunging to within 500 feet of the ground. His head was ringing from the blows that he had received against the side of the cockpit. By sheer strength and a lot of luck, he fought the storm for five more miles, keeping his power low and raising it only when the stalling horn blared above the roar of the turbulence. Nursing the light aircraft in this manner, he had been able to get out of the storm. "It was pure violence right to the ground," he said. "I'll never forget it."

The inquiry then turned to the story of pilot Norman Ramsay. His past career was laid bare, his negligence, his lack of alertness, his discharge by Trans-Canada Air Lines.

Then came a bombshell

While the investigation was in progress, the Montreal and Toronto newspapers learned that Ramsay had been taking psychiatric treatments since his TCA crash. Apparently he was trying to learn why a man of his ability would fly an aircraft into the ground, especially after the warning of his capable first officer.

The press discovered that the pilot's doctor was Dr. Bernard R. Raginsky of Montreal, president of the International Society for Clinical and Experimental Hypnosis. He was soon summoned to appear before the three-man Board of Enquiry, which included Captain C. D. Lamb of Trans-Canada Air Lines and also a member of the Canadian Air Line Pilots' Association, and Lucien Beauregard and P. E. Halsey, of the Department of Transport.

Dr. Raginsky had only recently delivered a major paper on hypnosis to a convention in Chicago and had leaked the news that a top airline pilot had been under treatment by him for years in order to find out the cause of the crash of an aircraft he was piloting.

Professional ethics had prevented Dr. Raginsky from revealing to the convention that Ramsay was the pilot under treatment. But now the newspapers put two and two together.

Questioned closely by the board, Dr. Raginsky stated that Capt. Norman Ramsay was "too emotionally sick to fly."

"I told him there was only one logical conclusion to his case . . . ground yourself forever . . . I told him . . . forever."

At this point a heated exchange of words took place between the solicitors of Maritime Central, the government, the pilots' association representatives, and the sleuths of the Quebec attorney general's department concerning the testimony of this doctor. Through it all, Dr. Raginsky defended his right to keep Ramsay's case confidential on the basis of the doctor-patient relationship. However, there were those who disagreed with the psychiatrist, on the ground that a pilot's mental health is a matter of national safety and therefore releases a doctor from his oath of professional secrecy.

In his concluding evidence, Dr. Raginsky revealed that Capt. Ramsay had also suffered severe emotional distress when changing altitude levels in flight. "His judgment would become unbalanced during these altitude changes," concluded the doctor. "I just told him flatly he couldn't be cured . . . stop flying."

After long intensive probing of all aspects of the disaster, the board had a few official remarks to make concerning the ill-fated flight. The flight had been overloaded when it left London. The crew was fatigued, having been on constant 24-hour duty and airborne for nineteen hours prior to the crash. Ramsay was guilty of a grave error in judgment when he failed to refuel at Quebec city and continued with only 122 gallons left in the tanks, and thus without sufficient range remaining to circumnavigate the thunderstorm.

The probable cause of the crash: severe turbulence encountered while flying in a violent thunderstorm which caused the loss of control of the aircraft, ending with its plunge into the ground.

The day after the disaster, August 12, 1957, the brother-in-law of army veteran Charles Granby, who was killed in the crash, received a postcard at his Hamilton, Ontario, home, sent from London two days before.

All it said was: "Hope to see you soon . . . flying is for the birds."

Birds don't fly in thunderstorms.

The Canopy of Air 2

ONLY THE CONVULSIONS of a summer thunderstorm could cause such violence.

When Brutel Seurremen had heard the frightening metallic noise high up in the storm clouds above him, the noise that sounded like tin banging against trees, he was listening to the death throes of a modern airliner being shaken to destruction. It was as though a giant hand had clutched the DC-4 about the middle and then playfully tossed it up and down, several hundred feet at a time.

"Just like an earthquake," Brutel later testified.

Yet this Maritime Central Airways disaster is only one in a long line of unnecessary and sometimes unexplainable air tragedies caused when pilots, knowingly or unknowingly, defy thunderstorms.

Early man undoubtedly retreated into the furthest recesses of his cave when lightning struck the earth and thunder shook the land. Primitive man devised stories to account for the mysteries of nature. These tales were simple explanations of the sun, moon, stars, winds and rain. Unable to distinguish between the human and the inanimate, man invested mountains and rivers, serpents and cats with mystic powers. Gradually worship was transferred from the object itself to the mysterious life power associated with it, and later to a single personality vested with that power. For instance, Zeus, the Greek deity, first became the sky, then a force within the sky, and, later on, a great god with sky powers.

The mysteries of the sky, the strange sights at night, the hissing sounds, meteor trails, comets, northern lights, as well as the cloud galleons of the day with the massive storms which they spawned, suddenly became explainable. The gods were at work or play. They were happy or angry as the case might be. The happenings in the sky were given meaning, and the most respected and most powerful gods thus became those who terrorized or blessed the world from above. Greek, Roman, Chinese, Indian, African, Norse, and many other cultures credited the gods of the sky with the greatest powers.

Although the ancients could explain that Vulcan of the Romans, Vestis of the Greeks, and Thor of the Norse playfully created thunderbolts on anvils in the sky, they nevertheless were terrorized by thunder and lightning. It meant the gods were angry at the earth or that they were fighting one another. Norsemen believed that rain fell when the rain god triumphed over the dry god, that winter was due to the triumph of the frost god over the other gods that controlled the heavens. Thor fashioned Odin's spear on the anvil. The strokes of his hammer were the thunder, and the sparks from his forge the lightning.

How strange that the loveliest of all cloud formations can be so dangerous and so beautiful; so soft and fluffy on the outside and so charged with atomic power within that the mass of turbulent air, laced with ice and rain, can suck a 125-ton airliner into its maw, crunch it like an eggshell, and scatter its fragments over a score of square miles.

The canopy of atmosphere above the earth is not a motionless sea of air. It is a vast ocean, vibrant and alive, constantly distorted by swift currents and colossal waves with tremendous crests and deep invisible troughs.

The crests are the mountains of air that rise above the surrounding mass. Because these crests have more air than the mass which surrounds them, they exert a great deal of pressure on the earth below. This is known as a high-pressure area and is recorded on our delicate earth instruments as it appears overhead and moves across the land. The winds spiral outward from this high-pressure mass, permitting the upper air to fill in the gaps below. As the upper air descends, it gets warmer and tends to compress itself. A system of this kind brings clear dry air down to the land, accompanied by blue skies and sunshine. Pilots often refer to the high-pressure systems as "blue bubbles," and that's exactly what they are.

Flying through high-pressure areas can be utterly delightful. The air is relatively smooth, the skies are clear, and the visibility is often unlimited. Pilots, particularly those who fly the North Atlantic, seek out the high-pressure systems and ride the clockwise winds with the special exhilaration that fine flying weather provides.

But, like the surface of the restless ocean, the crests in the air are followed by troughs in the ever-changing atmospheric sea. These great valleys are known as low-pressure areas. They sag because they have less air than the surrounding mass. Therefore, they exert only a low pressure on the land below.

The weather in a low-pressure system is generally stormy and unsettled. The winds surrounding low-pressure areas blow inward, sweeping accumulations of warm moist air into the troughs, and then, because warm air rises, the inbound mass of moist warm air climbs steadily upward to the cooler altitudes. There it condenses into clouds and subsequently turns into rain.

It is in these areas of low pressure that all the storms of the earth are spawned, including tornadoes, typhoons, thunderstorms, and hurricanes. Whatever the name, they are all systems of varying intensities that dot the atmospheric sea above the earth, and their distribution and their movements are controlled by the tremendous masses of cold air which swirl across the Arctic and Antarctic regions and over the warm oceans, steamy jungles, and hot, dry deserts of the tropics and subtropics.

Tremendous wind systems carry great masses of cold dry air

from the Poles toward the warmer climates of the tropics. Sometimes these winds are called jet streams as they speed out of the north and out of the Antarctic regions at speeds upward of 100 knots an hour. Meanwhile, other colossal systems of air move along the tropical zones and are diverted northward in the northern hemisphere and southward in the southern hemisphere by the motion of the earth.

Eventually the cold and dry air streams collide with the warm, moist masses. These collisions create the weather patterns of the world.

Modern weather forecasting can locate and plot the motion of the high- and low-pressure systems across the continents. But only within the past year or so, as a result of weather observance by satellites, have forecasters been able to plot the movements of the earth-girdling jet streams that move eight miles above the earth between high- and low-pressure areas. The plotting of these vast rivers of air helps the weathermen predict, much more accurately than before, the storms that cause havoc to the land and to aircraft flying above it.

Sometimes the great systems of cool air collide with the systems of warm moist air at great speed, and the violence which results is greater than the energy emitted by a 50-megaton atomic bomb. On other occasions, the collision is mild and well-mannered, merging with little sound or fury. The leading edges of these great movements of air are known to the weathermen as frontal systems. Pilots call them "fronts." Similarly, low-pressure systems are called "lows," and high-pressure systems are called "highs."

Fronts are changeable and unpredictable, according to the speed at which they are moving and the *dominance* they have been able to exert over the other masses of atmosphere around them. They occur in four categories: *cold, warm, occluded, stationary*.

Let's examine each one for a moment.

A *cold front* occurs when a mass of cool air rushes over the land in a great hurry and meets the warm air mass lazily moving from the tropical zones. The cool air forces the warm air upward, sometimes to tremendous heights, causing the violent convulsions that we see as thunderstorms. Such eruptions are brief and dramatic. When the violence subsides, the air behind the collision is cooler, and scattered powder-puff clouds dot the sky, replacing the violent and tormented heavens with beauty and grace.

The *warm front* is the leading edge of a slow-moving mass of warm air which eventually overtakes a cold-air accumulation. When this occurs, the warm air, which has less mass than the cold air, moves up and over it. Whole sections of the country are often covered by the dense cloud formations formed by these meetings, which bring dreary wet weather that hangs around for days on end.

An *occluded front* is created when a cold front, with the dominance of a bold stallion, overtakes and subdues a warm front high in the atmosphere. Dreary weather again results, and frequent showers move slowly over the countryside sometimes dropping prodigious amounts of rain.

When this weather pattern cannot get enough energy to move, it bogs down and remains in place for considerable time. It is then called a *stationary front.*

Flying through warm, occluded or stationary fronts can often be extremely uncomfortable to passengers in modern airliners. Cells of warm air charged with moisture create uneven masses in the flight path and bumpiness results. Frequently, when these fronts are charged with humidity but with little or no internal movement of air, flying is simple. The aircraft is often wrapped in a blanket of gray sun-filled haziness or blue-gray and black still air.

There are many spectacular convulsions created by the collision of the warm and cold fronts. Tornadoes are without doubt the most frightening because they are extremely violent and destructive. Their dark funnel clouds contain wind velocities as high as 300 miles an hour, and the violent updrafts within these funnels can often be as high as 200 miles an hour. Tornadoes develop in the southeast of a stormy low-pressure area, and are often accompanied by thunder and lightning and

Tornadoes are dangerous to aircraft on the ground, as well as to those approaching a landing while tornado-filled squall lines are passing over the flight path. As many as thirteen tornadoes have been photographed at the base of a single black cloud. In this photo, an Air Force plane is circling near a tornado in Okinawa, before attempting a landing near the snaking funnel. (U. S. Air Force photo)

frequently by hail. The only safe refuge from a tornado is below ground level.

There have been records of tornadoes appearing in the blackness of thunderstorms and it is quite possible that airplane disasters that have occurred in thunderstorms may have been caused by tornadoes within their masses. However, this is conjecture. Nevertheless, radar images of hurricanes have often turned up tiny white threads winding through the storm near its turbulent center, and these images have been identified as tornadoes. Tornadoes almost always develop between the base of the thunderclouds and the ground. They are rarely a threat to modern airliners, but are lethal to small aircraft flying under thunderstorms.

It is extremely dangerous for an airliner to take off into a thunderstorm because of the possible danger from tornadoes. Yet, despite this danger, many do take off under such conditions.

Hurricanes and typhoons are dangerous storms, but because they can be accurately predicted and traced by modern weather forecasting, they are not serious hazards to commercial flying. This does not apply to the brave U. S. Navy pilots who fly into them to determine their course and their winds.

Yet pilots of the Hurricane Hunters of Jacksonville, Florida, will tell you they would rather fly into the teeth of a raging hurricane than fly into the jaws of a summer thunderstorm, particularly a thunderstorm moving over the hot land mass of the Middle West.

"I've got a better than even chance in a hurricane . . . but I have none in a thunderstorm," one pilot of the Navy's Early Warning Squadron said recently.

Paradoxically, from the most beautiful of all cloud formations, the towering fleecy white castles of the loveliest summer day, come the worst tempests of them all. It takes a certain combination of temperature, humidity, and wind movement to create the tremendous billowy cumulus clouds, which, as they rise to the great heights of 20,000 to 30,000 feet, become cumulo-nimbus—the weatherman's term for thunderclouds.

On a hot summer day, such cumulus and cumulo-nimbus cloud formations are delightful to see but dangerous for flying because of the rapidly ascending currents of hot air, which cause wind shear and turbulence. The smoothest air in this case is above the clouds, preferably in the clear channels between the castles. (Photo by James Yarnell)

Beautiful anvils in the sky indicate the dissipation stages of thunderstorms. Under those overhanging ledges of cloud, hail showers are often found. Torrential rains, lightning, and ice storms rage within the swirling vapors. (U. S. Weather Bureau photo)

The familiar anvil top—the "Anvil of the Gods"—is formed when the rising powder puffs are flattened by the stable air of the upper atmosphere, which in turn prevents the clouds from rising higher and smooths them into a table-top line. The top of the anvil is the extreme terminal of the column of hot air which creates the imposing castles. It is interesting to know, incidentally, that at the top of every column of hot air a cloud is formed in the sky.

A study of the interior of a thunderstorm doesn't always bring the same explanation from scientists and weathermen. However, all agree that the ponderous cloud masses contain many extremely unstable cells of turbulent energy. The inner cells of the storm are torn by violent updrafts and fantastic downdrafts. Water droplets are continuously being carried aloft, turn to hail in the upper reaches, become heavy and fall downward, turning to snow and then to rain as they reach the warmer altitudes. Sometimes the hailstones are so large they never get a chance to melt before they bombard the earth below. They are often large enough and propelled with such force that they dent the heavy-gauge steel of automobile roofs. It doesn't require much imagination to realize what they can do to the thin duraluminum of a modern airliner, much less to the fabric of a light plane.

A ground observer of a thunderstorm will frequently be subjected to a sudden and heavy downpour of rain—followed at once by a lightning flash and then by a clap of thunder. However, all three actually take place at the same time. The sudden rise in condensation from the increased violence in the cloud triggers the electrical discharge, and the difference in time between the lightning, thunder, and the torrential rainfall is just a matter of their different rates of travel.

Lightning travels at the speed of light, 186,000 miles per second. And some of the bolts have been measured at more than 20 miles in length. (The greatest recorded lightning current consisted of five surges containing an estimated 345,000 amperes.) Thunder sound moves at 1,100 feet per second, and rain about 20 to 25 feet downward per second.

Navy hurricane hunters work closely with the U. S. Weather Bureau to discover and track dangerous tropical storms in the Caribbean. Not a few lives have been lost in doing so. This photo shows an F2H Banshee of the Navy's Photographic Squadron, based at Jacksonville, Florida, taking photographs of a hurricane's eye. (U. S. Navy photo)

This is an excellent photo of a mature thunderstorm, known to pilots and weathermen as a cumulo-nimbus cloud formation. Its violent updrafts have not yet reached the tremendous heights where stable air will halt the onrushing drafts and smooth the cloud tops into the familiar anvils. (U. S. Weather Bureau photo)

Cumulo-nimbus clouds, stretching a hundred miles wide north of this airport, disclose a massive storm on the march. Cumulo-nimbus clouds are sometimes hidden by other, nonviolent cloud formations. (U. S. Weather Bureau photo)

When lightning strikes close by, the heaviest crash of thunder comes from the trunk of the blast, while the crackling that follows emanates from the branches as they arc through the clouds. It is possible to estimate the distance to the oncoming storm by timing the intervals between the lightning and the thunder. It takes a sound wave about 72 seconds to travel 15 miles. The time interval between the flash and the rumble is rarely more than 70 to 80 seconds, because the sound of thunder begins to rise upward from the ground and can rarely be heard more than 15 or 16 miles from the source.

It is estimated that each year lightning kills some 400 persons in the United States, and injures 1,000 others. Statistics reveal that most people are killed or injured by lightning in the rural areas of the country. Men are struck down five times more frequently than women, another solid indication that it is safer indoors than outdoors during a thunderstorm, since men tend to continue their work in the farm fields and golfers plunge ahead with their game despite the black skies and the ominous rumblings from above. Insurance firms have estimated that one third of all lightning deaths occur to people who take shelter under trees. A single lightning bolt is so powerful that agriculture authorities have recorded an instance when a bolt struck an elm tree under which was standing a herd of sixty Holstein dairy cattle. Every animal was instantly killed. The loss of this herd wiped out a successful dairy farmer.

It isn't often that there are witnesses to lightning strikes. However, there have been a few. In 1940, a number of people residing in the town of Lovettsville, Virginia, watched a DC-3 flying under a heavy cloud, while sheets of rain curtained the countryside. Suddenly, with a blinding flash, a single lightning bolt arced across the cloud base, struck the airliner, and continued to the ground—all in a microsecond. The DC-3 lurched from the strike, nosed down and plummeted into the ground, carrying its crew and a full load of passengers to their deaths.

Some pilots take off from the runways right into the very teeth of thunderstorms. In October 1961, two airliners—one an *Electra* and the other a DC-6B, both operated by famous U. S.

A typical late spring thunderstorm rolled over Boston on May 24, 1962, setting up this brilliant pyrotechnic display. Note the brilliant explosive flashes where the lightning bolts strike the high, pointed objects in their pathway to the ground. This spectacular photo was taken by Philip Preston of the Boston Globe. (U. S. Weather Bureau photo)

Until it starts to rain, a cloud has no electrical field because the electrical charge carried within each droplet is surrounded by ionized air molecules of the opposite charge. Neutralizing ions travel upward, permitting the charged droplets to build up enough negative charge so that a discharge must take place. This photo shows the many exchanges of electricity that take place between a cloud and the earth in a second or so. (U. S. Weather Bureau photo)

flag lines—took off from the municipal airport at Orlando, Florida, into the blackness of low scud clouds at the end of the southeast runway. Rain blackened the landscape beyond, and forks of lightning played a symphony of light along the perimeter of the field. Both aircraft veered left after take-off, banked very sharply over homes on the east side of the airport, and worked northward at a very low altitude before disappearing into the blackness. As a passenger in the DC-6B, I was concerned about the weather conditions even before the take-off but what was I to do? Should I stay in Orlando until the weather cleared and perhaps have to wait until the next day? I was making an important connection in Atlanta and I always play ball with the airline schedule and the judgment of the pilot. After the take-off, there was very slight turbulence, lightning was flashing vividly on either side of the plane but luckily we were not hit. We found a rift in the clouds and went up through it to clear skies.

Incidents like these occur frequently and nothing serious happens. Yet they indicate the insufficient regard that many pilots have for thunderstorms and the lightning which these storms energize. However, as will be shown later, a take-off under exactly these same conditions can end with appalling results.

James Foy, veteran pilot of Trans-Canada Air Lines, former president of the Canadian Air Line Pilots' Association and much-respected by the Air Line Pilots' Association (ALPA) of the U. S., recalls that he took off from New York's Idlewild Airport one night in 1956 at the controls of a Vickers *Viscount*. There were no thunderstorms in the region, but low scud clouds occasionally scurried across the field and considerable rain had been reported north of the airport. The visibility was good and no storm trouble was anticipated. Captain Foy eased the turboprop down the runway, lifted off easily, held level for a few moments, and then eased into a shallow climb over the perimeter of the field. Suddenly, and without warning, a lightning bolt struck the *Viscount*, blinding the crew and the passengers.

Captain Foy elected to turn around, land, and inspect his

Over Tell City, Indiana, a Lockheed Electra like the one shown here tangled with severe clear-air turbulence associated with a low-pressure system over Michigan. Nacelle oscillation was set up as a result of the turbulence at 18,000 feet, and the magnificent aircraft crashed. Design changes in the aircraft cost Lockheed some $129 million. (Lockheed Aircraft photo)

aircraft after such a jolt. What he found convinced him that lightning can be extremely dangerous to an aircraft in flight. He found that metal fusing had taken place between one of the ailerons and the wing. It was slight enough not to have caused a failure in the aircraft's control system, but had the bolt been stronger it could have caused disaster.

Wing Commander John Briggs, pilot and much decorated commander of the World War II *Mosquito "F for Freddie,"* recalled, a week before he died in his plane, that the most frightening moment he had experienced in all his years of fighting and aerial reconnaissance was on the night he was en route to Berlin, flying at high altitude through a thunderstorm.

"The wings began to glow and then fire began to dance along the wings," he said. "Lightning flashed all about us, and blinded us so badly that my navigator couldn't read our instruments. Then the cockpit began to fill with fire—St. Elmo's fire— dancing over the instruments, covering my control wheel. It was terrible and I'll never fly in the region of thunderstorms again. The St. Elmo's fire didn't harm us any, nor disturb the continued flight of my aircraft. But it was an unnerving experience and the worst I have ever known."

Wing Commander Briggs contended that pilots should never underestimate the mental hazards of St. Elmo's fire and lightning. "When panic takes over in the cockpit," he said, "rain, icing, lightning, turbulence seem to worsen. You're blinded. You can't see. You are numbed by the experience. You can't tell if you are in level flight or whether you are going downward with your air speed building up dramatically and dangerously. After one lightning flash in front of the cockpit at night, you cannot see what you are doing for a full minute afterwards."

Nowadays, due to the increased knowledge of what triggers lightning in thunderstorms, it is often possible to ascertain with reasonable sureness when lightning is most likely to be present. A pilot must be prepared to face a lightning strike when St. Elmo's fire begins to play over the plane's fuselage, along the wings, and around the instrument panel and controls. The first thing he must do is to reel in his trailing aerial, if the plane carries one. Leaving the aerial out is a good way of introducing lightning into the passenger compartment and into the flight deck.

Lightning usually occurs in cloud layers where the temperatures are between 15 and 32 degrees Fahrenheit.

The possibility of a strike can be minimized by reducing the speed of the aircraft. Pilots should attempt to protect themselves against temporary blindness by turning on cockpit lights to full brilliance.

Acoustic shock is another sinister item to expect. A near lightning strike can deafen a pilot. Therefore, earphones should be worn in such a manner as to be slightly ahead of the ears and pressing against the cheekbone. Volume of the radio receivers should be reduced to the barest minimum and, in most situations, only one of the crew at the controls should wear the earphones—just in case.

3

"One of Our Aircraft is Missing"

WHEN AN AIRCRAFT ENGINE catches fire in flight, whether the plane crashes or not, new maintenance procedures are immediately instituted by all airlines. Modifications are hurried from the drafting room to the manufacturing line. Firewalls are extended. Air intakes located near electrical heat are rerouted. Fuel lines are strengthened, and so on.

When a collision between two airplanes occurs on one of the crowded corridors of the sky, new rules are written into air regulations, and flying procedures are reviewed and changed in a constant battle to maintain the highest standard of safe flying possible.

When a passenger airliner fails to become airborne or crashes shortly after take-off, whether it runs into birds or the trouble is caused by control failure, entirely new mechanical procedures are immediately invoked. Airframe and engine manufacturers are called on the carpet and urged to change their manufacturing methods, upgrade their quality control, and revitalize their testing procedures to take care of scores of variables that can occur.

And when a qualified pilot becomes flustered and goofs up an instrument landing approach, or collapses an undercarriage, or fails to stop on the runway in time, steps are taken at once to beef up pilot training, concentrating on the areas that involve safer landings.

No matter what goes wrong with the aircraft and no matter what goes wrong with the man at the controls, Federal aviation agencies, the airlines, airframe and engine manufacturers, and the ever-watchful Air Line Pilots' Association all move quickly and positively to force corrective action. They do a terrific job, leaving no stone unturned, and flying is safer and saner today only because of their militant and continuous efforts.

Yet when a pilot flies his airliner into the jaws of a thunderstorm, kills himself, his crew, and the hapless men, women, and children who purchased tickets and just happened to get on his flight, there follows the usual appalling impact on the public. *What can be done?*

Well, first of all, little can be changed so far as the aircraft is concerned. It has already had plenty of structural integrity built into it and besides, no practical changes could give it sufficient strength to fly safely through a dangerous thunderstorm or into a tornado.

What about radar?

Today all modern airliners are radar equipped but this hasn't stopped thunderstorm tragedies.

Then what about improved weather bulletins?

How improved can they get? There is little evidence on record these days that pilots have failed to get all available information as to the possibility of dangerous and turbulent weather before they embark on their flights, and they usually receive up-to-the-minute information of weather changes as the flight progresses. During the past few years, the quality of weather forecasting at airports has reached a highly commendable level. It is far more accurate than public weather forecasting.

Does this mean the essential safety ingredient is the pilot?

Absolutely. During flight, in combination with weather bulletins and radar, he alone is the judge of whether to fly or not to fly into dangerous cloud formations.

Airlines can beat the drums about safer flying because of radar, smoother travel without turbulence, and embellish this with all the other devices of modern advertising, but their pronouncements are little more than words from the imaginative pencil of a copywriter if a few pilots continue to show unconcern for bad weather.

No matter how excellent the weather forecasting service, how comprehensive the preflight and en route briefings, how marvelous the modern electronic gadgetry, a few pilots have ignored the warnings, the briefings, and the obvious indications of present danger, choosing instead to forget years of training and millions of miles of experience to fly into dangerous thunderstorms.

Thunderstorms present flight problems that should cause even the most experienced instrument pilot, flying the best of aircraft, to plan his flight with special care when thunderstorms are forecast along his route. Before taking off, he should study carefully all the information that is available concerning the particular situation. The best plan is to avoid thunderstorms.

This passage is part of a lengthy summary on thunderstorm flying contained in a booklet entitled *Weather Ways*, published by the Department of Transport of the Canadian Government for commercial and military pilots. Its common sense is not limited by geographical boundaries.

Yet, despite such persistent warnings, briefings and intense training, pilots continue to underestimate the Anvil of the Gods. It has been suggested many times that pilots may be reluctant to cancel a flight, or delay a flight, or turn back because of fear of being called "chicken." In the past, some pilots may have been under company pressure to maintain schedules and not let little things like storms hold up their progress.

However, most pilots and most airlines agree that a pair of silver wings is no mandate to take chances.

United Air Lines has boasted that not one of its planes has ever suffered hail damage, and the reason for this is an intense pilot education program which warns of the danger of overhanging clouds of thunderstorms, and the danger of hail within the storms themselves. As a result, United pilots circumnavigate thunderstorms to avoid even the most remote chance of hail.

Northwest Airlines has had unfortunate experiences with thunderstorms, having lost three and maybe four airliners with heavy casualties in areas of thunderstorm activity. Two recent disasters were in aircraft equipped with radar, but this didn't seem to have made any difference. Two earlier crashes were before the days of radar-equipped airliners.

Take the case of Flight 2501.

Veteran pilot Robert Linn, tall, handsome, thirty-five-year-old captain of Northwest Airlines, was experienced in every type of flying machine from wheezing puddle jumpers to giant four-engine transports. He flew one of the busiest routes in the nation from New York westward to the cities of the Midwest. He was considered a capable, knowledgeable pilot. If he had not been considered so, he wouldn't have been flying four-engine aircraft for Northwest.

Yet Captain Robert Linn is a classic example of a pilot who, aware of the danger ahead, continued onward, ignoring the decisions of other pilots until it was too late. At 8 P.M. on the pleasant evening of June 24, 1950, Captain Linn and his co-pilot, Vern Wolfe, who was also thirty-five years of age, talked with the weather forecaster at La Guardia Airport, on Long Island, northeast of the bustling island of Manhattan.

Linn and Wolfe were preparing to fly to their home city of Minneapolis on one of Northwest's nonstop New York to Minneapolis flights. Air Traffic Control provided the two pilots with the route, New York to Pittsburgh, to Cleveland, over Detroit and onward to Grand Rapids, across Lake Michigan to Milwaukee, and thence to the twin cities, home base of Northwest.

The weather forecaster advised the two pilots that flying conditions seemed good as far as Detroit, but then they might encounter unstable air conditions and possibly severe turbulence over the hot land mass. Beyond this, he predicted thunderstorms over Wisconsin, Illinois, and Michigan, as a cold front moved slowly southeastward from Canada, knifing into the hot humid air masses ahead of it. The picture was a perfect portrait for violent thunderstorm activity: unstable, hot, humid air and a cold front on the move. Both pilots studied the weather bulletins and the en route weather reports amassed from other aircraft before picking up their heavy satchels of maps and procedures and heading for a sleek DC-4 parked on the tarmack in front of the busy La Guardia terminal.

It was 8:15 P.M.

Captain Linn looked at the sun, low on the northwest horizon, and knew he would be following its beckoning beacon in just a few minutes. He walked around the aircraft, making his customary visual inspection, and then went aboard, chatting briefly with Bonnie Ann Feldman, pretty blonde stewardess of Northwest, just turned twenty-five years.

"We've got a full one tonight," she said. "Fifty-five passengers."

"Good," said Linn and made his way up the narrow aisle to the flight deck, where Wolfe was already at his preliminary cockpit checkouts. Linn settled back in his seat, adjusted it, and checked the fuel load chart, approved it, signed, and then began the many preparations necessary to activate the four Pratt & Whitney power plants. The number-three engine coughed into action first with a tornado of oily smoke and the three others followed. As the No SMOKING and FASTEN YOUR SEAT BELTS signs were flashed on, Miss Feldman reported all passengers aboard and accounted for. Capt. Linn waved to the ramp agent, brought the engines to gustier thrums, and the DC-4 headed for the warm-up apron in the southeast section of the La Guardia field.

It was 8:30 P.M.

Captain Linn and Wolfe made their pre-take-off checks; brought the engines to full power, noted the oil heat, the manifold pressure, switched the banks of magnetos, and checked to see that the fuel gauges were registering correctly. The engines were then idled. The control tower, located to Linn's left in the La Guardia terminal, gave permission for the take-off. The four arms of the propeller pitch controls were moved full forward to provide the greatest thrust possible from the whirling blades. The fuel and air mixture was activated to full rich and the four throttles moved forward quickly. The huge DC-4 came to vibrant, noisy life and started down the runway, slow at first, but quickly gathering speed as the 3,500-foot mark was passed. The wings, loaded with 2,500 gallons of high-octane fuel, lifted the plane slowly as the roar of the engines reverberated from the apartments that lined the south end of the field.

The aircraft, now free of the ground, tucked her wheels and Capt. Linn made a slight bank to the left over the East River and took her into a steady northwest climb at 500 feet per minute.

"Off at eight thirty-five," Wolfe radioed the control tower.

Still roaring loudly, as only a DC-4 can roar, the Northwest flight crossed over the Harlem district of Manhattan while passengers on the left side of the aircraft gaped at the incomparable view on this hazy June evening. Millions of lights sparkled like oriental jewels in the gathering twilight. A minute later, the flight was over the Hudson and the land beyond lay dark in the shadows. At cruising altitude twenty minutes later, the heavy plane settled down to a throaty purr and the air was smooth and comforting.

The lights of Pittsburgh were the first to brighten the gathering night, and then a short time later Cleveland twinkled beneath the wings, the dark shoreline of Lake Erie visible by its stygian blackness and the casual reflections from shore buildings. Occasionally a ship's lights would stand out in the darkness.

Ahead on the horizon glowed the city of Detroit. Capt. Linn would fly his DC-4 some distance west of the city to cross the radio range at Willow Run Airport where he would make another of the many radio reports necessary in his flight. Far to the west and northwest, perhaps as much as 280 miles away, lightning played among the invisible cloud castles and returned its light in a glowing series of flashes often called sheet lightning. It was a friendly warning that under the distant panorama of deep orange color there were thunderstorms moving.

Westward from Detroit, the DC-4 began to shake and creak.

Warm currents of air, heated during the day along the ground, were moving upward into the cold atmosphere and their ascending columns began to shake the aircraft. As the flight progressed across Michigan the turbulence in the unstable moist air began to worsen and the passengers secured themselves with their safety belts. The increasing turbulence, combined with the lightning flashes ahead in the western abyss of darkness, was an indication that the pilot could expect thunderstorm activity in his path.

But Capt. Linn flew ever onward into the danger signs.

Linn and Wolfe, and all other qualified airline pilots, knew that turbulence is caused by the motion of air from eddies and vertical currents and is very important in the world of flying because it can produce unusual and dangerous stresses in the aircraft, and create instrument errors and pilot fatigue. Turbulence can be caused by a multitude of weather conditions, but, no matter what the cause, the degree of turbulence is always determined by the degree of stability of the air. The nature of the causes may evolve from frontal conditions, mechanical agencies, thermal conditions, and a phenomenon known as wind shear.

What are these mechanical agencies?

They may be trees, hills, buildings, mountains, houses, or even the hangars on the perimeter of an airport. The friction between the air and the ground sets up a series of eddies near the surface and, as a result, choppiness while flying is quickly noticeable. In cases where there are strong winds combined with unstable air conditions, large eddies can swirl around these mechanical agencies and be carried downwind for several hundred yards. The disturbances thus created in the regular horizontal flow of air over the ground cause the air to blow in gusts and lulls. The weather is said to be gusty and extremely violent air conditions may result, particularly if the ground is rough. Sudden increases in the wind lasting for several minutes are referred to as squalls and indicate that severe turbulence exists above.

Black and ugly and seething with energy, cumulus clouds swirl in the unstable atmosphere to form isolated thunderstorms. They form quickly, sometimes trapping the unwary pilot. (Photo by James Yarnell)

Many an airline passenger has been seated comfortably, enjoying an effortless and smooth take-off, looking down at the houses, trees and buildings sliding away beneath, when suddenly the aircraft will pitch and yaw, dive and rear, in a series of sickening gyrations before smoothing out a few minutes later. This is the kind of turbulence caused by mechanical agencies. In flying it is generally brief but spectacular.

Turbulence in the air also can be caused by what the weatherman calls a thermal agency. This is the most common cause of unsettled air and is created by the heating of the earth's surface by the sun. On a beautiful summer day, usually when there is little wind, the ground is strongly heated. Bubbles of hot air, sometimes hundreds of yards in diameter, form next to the ground and then climb steadily upward, one after the other. The upward current of warm air increases in speed and doesn't smooth out until its temperature is the same as the temperature of the surrounding air mass. It then loses speed and comes to a stop.

Flying through these vertical warm currents can be rough indeed, particularly for small business and personal aircraft, unable to climb to the cooler air masses above. Commercial passenger planes will shake and rumble, sometimes quite violently, while landing or taking off through these convection currents, on even the loveliest days.

The force of these columns of air depends mostly on the extent to which the ground is heated and this, in turn, depends on the nature of the surface. For instance, barren surfaces, such as rocky, sandy or hard-clay wastes, are heated more rapidly than land covered with grass or trees or farm crops. Water surfaces are heated less rapidly, and the difference in heating causes those heavy bumps when crossing a shoreline on hot days. Bumps have been reported as high as 14,000 feet by pilots crossing from land to ocean, and are particularly noticeable over the New Jersey shore en route to La Guardia and Idlewild Airports.

Thermal turbulence is also characteristic of the lower levels of a cold air mass that is moving over a warm surface, as when a cold mass moves over water during wintertime. Heating from the water causes an unstable air condition and sets up convection currents. This, in turn, creates squally winds and very bumpy flying conditions near the surface.

The turbulence which is associated with a frontal system may be caused by two factors: the uplift of warmer air, forced aloft with great speed by the sloping edge of the front, or by friction between the opposing air currents of the two air masses. The updrafts and downdrafts in the warmer air are strongly marked when the warm air is moist, and this is particularly true when thunderstorms begin to develop. Temperature and wind changes warn the pilot of the presence of a frontal system and of the turbulence which is associated with such vast opposing masses of air in rapid motion.

There is yet another cause of turbulence in the air. This is associated with marked changes in wind velocity at various heights. For example, the difference in speed between slow moving air and the rapidly moving jet stream often encountered by jet aircraft can cause severe turbulence, even at the tremendous heights which are the ceilings of commercial airliners. The turbulence associated with these rivers of wind is known to weatherman and pilot as wind shear. On the clearest days and nights, flying can be rough and irritating, due to these wind shears.

In summing up this discussion of turbulence, it can be said that turbulence is a very reliable and valuable weather sign, in spite of being a nuisance. Choppiness indicates mechanical turbulence. Sustained jars indicate convection currents, and there is always a direct relationship between turbulence and other weather phenomena.

Captain Linn and his crew and fifty-five passengers were experiencing moderate turbulence over the state of Michigan— bumpiness caused by thermal currents in moist unstable air conditions. The appearance in the west of continuous lightning flashes and static disturbance in the earphones all indicated there could be trouble ahead.

This is a line squall, with high, gusting winds and low, menacing clouds that swirl toward the ground, marking the movement of a typical cold front across the face of the land. Sometimes, however, decks of stratus clouds hide the approaching cold front. Cumulonimbus clouds indicate that thunderstorms are associated with the front. (U. S. Weather Bureau photo)

Linn flew on toward Minneapolis. By this time, the passengers would be experiencing a very unsatisfactory flight and there would be a goodly number who wished they had taken a train.

The turbulence increased and Capt. Linn radioed that he was in moderate turbulence and requested permission from Air Traffic Control for a lower altitude to escape from the clouds on his flight path and seek solace closer to the ground, although that was not exactly the best place to escape thermal currents and mechanical turbulence.

Linn was granted permission to descend to 3,500 feet and he eased back on his power and brought the heavy DC-4 down to the lower level. It was quite apparent from this maneuver that Linn was intending to continue on into the display of pyrotechnics and try to escape the thunderstorms ahead of him by flying underneath them.

Linn was a much braver man than three of his fellow pilots with Northwest Airlines. In three other aircraft, they had each made a valiant attempt to shove their way through Michigan skies that night, but the turbulence and the threatening thunderstorm activity proved too much for their stomachs and their intelligence. All three sought safety at Detroit's Willow Run Airport, coming to roost while Linn bravely and foolhardily fought on. One of the planes which landed at Willow Run was a DC-4, similar to Linn's. The other two planes were twin-engined Martin 202's.

At 10:52 P.M. the flight radioed it was over Battle Creek, Michigan—halfway across the state. The flight estimated its arrival at Milwaukee, on the west side of Lake Michigan, at 11:27 P.M. Central Standard Time, and on the ground at Minneapolis at 1:23 A.M.

Less than five minutes after this communication, Capt. Linn reported to Milwaukee Air Traffic Control that he was in severe turbulence.

When a pilot has the courage to report he is flying in light turbulence, you can bet the passengers have seat belts on and are being well bumped. When he reports that he is flying in moderate turbulence, it means that the aircraft is flying through heavy stomach-turning vertical updrafts and downdrafts, groaning and shaking and causing fright among the most seasoned air travelers.

But when the pilot radios, as Linn did, that he is in severe turbulence, it means that he is in trouble. The plane would be bouncing all over the sky, yawing wildly, trying to shake itself loose from the currents that engulfed it. One can only feel pity for the unfortunate passengers at this moment, as they are slammed through the frightening blackness of the night, holding onto the seat rests, while their bodies strain and churn against the safety belts. Some would be ill, vomiting into their paper containers, without help from the stewardess, who would be strapped in her seat. The stench of the sick would contribute to the illness of others.

In an attempt to escape the turbulence, Capt. Linn managed to reach Milwaukee through the increasing static and asked for permission to get down another 1,000 feet to 2,500 feet, since he was now over the eastern Lake Michigan shoreline, on course, and just by the city of South Haven.

His request was denied. There was already too much air traffic on these lower altitudes.

It was the last message from the flight.

The DC-4, its red lights flashing in the rain, pitched onward into the turbulence for several more minutes.

At this point many a pilot would have turned back or changed direction in an attempt to circumnavigate the storm. But Linn apparently thought he could fly under the thunderstorm where the turbulence would not be so high that he would lose control of his aircraft. But Linn, in his preoccupation with flying the aircraft, may have forgotten one of the most important of all weather lessons. Severe gusts occur beneath the base of the thundercloud and the base of the cloud is dependent on the amount of humidity in the air. Since the air is moister over water, the cloud base drops lower, sometimes almost to the water itself, so that there is no escaping the severity of the gusts.

Not only gusts but violent downdrafts, as well as hail and icing, are common associates at these lower levels—a lethal combination if ever there was one.

A thunderstorm is made up of several cells in various stages of development with considerable connective clouds between them. Some storms may consist of only one cell, but a solitary cell does not grow to so great a height as one that is part of a multicellular system. As the storm develops, each successive cell grows to a greater height than the previous one.

The thunderstorm that enveloped Capt. Linn and his DC-4 had developed during the daytime heating of moist air. This type of storm is prominent during the hot days of spring and summer. During the late afternoon and evening, it begins to grow alarmingly and moves across the face of the land. The activity doesn't cease until the ground cools beneath it.

In the initial stage, every thunderstorm is a big cumulus cloud, white and billowy. At this stage a single updraft prevails in the cloud. The maximum vertical speed of this updraft usually occurs in the very topmost part of the cell and it is not unusual for the speed of this current to reach 3,000 feet per minute. At every level in this cloud, the temperature is higher than at the same level of surrounding air. The diameter of one cell may grow from one or two miles to as much as six miles.

From this single cell, the thunderstorm moves into its mature stage and spawns a number of cells, their updrafts penetrating to great heights where ice crystals become abundant and supercooled water droplets lead to the formation of hail and then rain.

The appearance of rain on the ground marks the transition from the initial stage to the mature stage, and the drag of this falling precipitation starts the downdraft moving.

At first, the downdraft is found only in the middle and lower levels of the cells, but it gradually increases in height and width, although it never quite reaches the tops of the clouds. The downflow of air spreads along the ground, bringing instant changes to surface weather condtions. During this

Cool air passing over the warm land in the hot subtropical regions forms summer clouds of this kind, shown here over Orlando, Florida. By afternoon the clouds are heavy with rain, and many of the clusters will form isolated thunderstorms. (U. S. Air Force photo)

stage, the cells may build up to 30,000 or 40,000 feet and in some regions have been found at 60,000 feet. Occasionally, the friction between the updrafts and the downdrafts at the front of the cells causes a rolling scud cloud to appear in front of the storm.

The mature stage of each cell usually lasts for fifteeen to thirty minutes and by the end of that time the other cells have moved up to take over.

Horizontally, the mass of cloud and its hidden cells may extend anywhere from 20 to 300 miles. The presence of the anvil—the Anvil of the Gods—always indicates that thunderstorm conditions exist and further reveals that at least one cell has reached its limit and is in a dissipating stage in the cold stable upper air.

When a cell is in the early cumulus or initial stage of development, a gentle inflow of wind takes place. Most people recognize this as the wind which blows toward the approaching thunderstorm. As the downdraft develops rapidly in the cell, its cold air spreads out along the surface of the ground undercutting the warm air in such a manner as to resemble a miniature cold front. Turbulence within the lower level of this spreading air is often severe, the gusts reaching out to a considerable distance ahead of the storm.

All these items present special problems to pilots, and these problems are associated with the individual cells within each storm. If a flight could be conducted through the clouds between the cells, there would be fairly smooth sailing. That is what radar is for. Its signals are reflected when they collide with water droplets in the cells; and, since turbulence is associated with rain, this indicates the area to be avoided. Hurricane Hunter pilots use this system to perfection, flying to the center of a vast tropical storm along the narrow passages between the spiral currents of rainfall. Likewise, commercial airline pilots, in planes equipped with weather radar, are trained to fly in the areas around the cells of rainfall. This can be tricky and the behavior of the cells can change. Some cells are not just straight up and down but angle off in other directions, usually rearward and upward from the leading edge of the storm.

This photograph shows cloud formations on a typical hot summer day, with one group of clouds gathering in the middle distance to form a cumulo-nimbus cell. Storms of this kind are most prominent in coastal regions when onshore winds prevail. (U. S. Navy photo)

The most beautiful clouds of a summer day are the fluffy cumulous build-ups that appear like galleons on a sea of blue. This is the first stage of the thunderstorm as the billowing cumulous cloud begins to form a cell of activity. (U. S. Weather Bureau photo)

Some pilots have been able to boast, before the days of radar, that they had safely flown through a thunderstorm. It simply meant they had been fortunate enough to be in a relatively quiet corridor between the cells.

During the active period of each cell, the cloud making up the cell is composed entirely of drafts—updrafts during the early stages and downdrafts during the later stages. The cell updraft is usually less than 25,000 feet across, although on some occasions it has reached out to 40,000 feet in width. During this advanced stage the updraft is usually above 10,000 feet.

Downdrafts are slower than updrafts and do not extend outward so far. They travel downward through the clouds, continuing below the base until they reach the ground and then spreading out horizontally. The speed of the downdraft in the rain reaches twenty feet a second and more. Aircraft making flying tests in thunderstorms have experienced displacements in their altitudes of 500 feet in at least half of all the drafts encountered. Therefore, a pilot trying to keep to his assigned airspace would be forced to take corrective action in more than half of the cells encountered, and, in doing so, he would be imposing extra stresses on the airframe of the aircraft and receive changes in altitude that could easily lead to dangerous stalls and dives.

The distance that an aircraft can be carried downward during flight beneath a cell depends on the extent and speed of the draft as well as the velocity of the aircraft. It is unlikely that an aircraft could be carried more than 1,500 to 2,000 feet by the downdraft alone. At heights of less than 2,000 feet over land and much lower over water, the downdraft usually reaches its maximum width but its speed is sometimes low. However, pilots must take great care in avoiding a nose-high attitude that could lead to a stall if a gust should be encountered. And gusts are irregular and unpredictable. Some gusts that have been measured below the base of the cloud are as severe as those within the cloud, and the severest of these gusts are found immediately after the rain commences.

This is what a thunderstorm looks like when flying over it. Turbulence can be moderate to extreme above these tops. (U. S. Air Force photo)

Since hail occurs most often between 10,000 and 15,000 feet, Capt. Linn likely was not bothered by this frightening associate of thunderstorms. He was fighting downdrafts and violent gusts at an altitude of 3,500 feet over the water, and his plane would not have to be shoved downward very far to hit the water. In such extreme gusts he would have no time whatsoever to recover either from sudden stalls or from as sudden dives.

It required only a basic knowledge of thunderstorms to predict what was going to happen to Capt. Linn and the DC-4.

When he failed to arrive over Milwaukee, Air Traffic Control attempted to locate him by radio, but the noise of the static was fearful, and it was believed that communication from the plane had been stopped only because of the storm. Linn, it was agreed, must have shut off his radio.

But the night wore on with no word from Linn, no word of the fate of the big DC-4 and the fifty-five storm-tossed passengers.

Milwaukee beamed a steady series of messages to the DC-4 without receiving an answer and finally, when it was considerably overdue and unreported, Northwest Airlines in Milwaukee was informed of the missing flight. When a flight is reported overdue and unreported, there is an immediate tendency on the part of airlines and air traffic controllers to clam up, hoping against hope that the aircraft will miraculously reappear. A nervous Northwest public relations official attempted to calm relatives and friends awaiting the long-delayed arrival of Flight 2501 by issuing a statement that the plane had enough fuel to stay aloft for twelve hours, whatever that meant.

Today, when an aircraft disappears off radar or fails to make a routine radio check en route, the newspapers are hot on the trail and the news is out long before the scheduled time of the plane's arrival in another city. But in 1950 radar surveillance was spotty and missing aircraft reports did not reach the inquisitive ears of the newspapers so rapidly.

Still, it was the morning newspapers that announced the probability of the nation's worst air disaster. Flight 2501, Northwest's popular air coach service from New York to Minneapolis and Seattle appeared to have gone down in a storm somewhere over Lake Michigan, and already a vast armada of ships and planes was being assembled to hunt for it. Hope was held out that the plane might have been ditched in the lake and the passengers have escaped in their life jackets or rafts. In fact, one of the first boats to defy the choppy lake found a lifebelt floating off Milwaukee. But any hope in this direction was soon dashed by the announcement of the Federal Aviation Agency that planes "now flying over Lake Michigan do not require life preservers since the flying time has been reduced to a scant 25 minutes."

The search continued all through June 25 and the next day, without a trace of the giant plane being found. Meanwhile scores of false reports of the aircraft being sighted poured in from both sides of the lake. All of them proved worthless; many were simply figments of the imagination.

Then, some 38 hours after Capt. Linn's last message, a U. S. Coast Guard cutter discovered a significant clue: a large oil slick on the water, ten miles due west of South Haven, Michigan.

This was the likeliest spot for the disaster, close to the area of Linn's last report. Carefully searching the confused waters, coast guardsmen found fragments of human bodies and scraps of paper from the aircraft's log. Floating in a small slick was a Salvation Army hymnbook. The largest piece of wreckage found measured 2 feet by 11 inches. The main fuselage of the DC-4 could not be located.

When one considers that Linn's last reported altitude was 3,500 feet and that only meager fragments of wreckage could be found, one can only imagine the tremendous force that clutched the DC-4 and hurled it into the lake.

Whatever befell pilots Linn and Wolfe in those last few seconds will never be known, but it is logical to assume they encountered gusts that either forced them into a stall or caused the aircraft to dive out of control into the lake. Had the DC-4 broken up in flight, as others had in thunderstorms, entire wing sections might have been found floating on the surface, made buoyant by their empty fuel cells. But this DC-4 must have struck the water with such tremendous force that the passengers were dissected into small fragments and metal parts were shredded to slivers.

Could Linn have collided with the scud cloud, rolling westward just ahead of the storm?

Perhaps. But it would appear that he moved through the leading edges of the squall, reporting the severe turbulence which he encountered, and then moved on into an active cell or the downdraft associated with it.

All pilots should remember what can occur behind those angry squall lines of advancing spring or summer thunderstorms. The lesson goes back far enough. It was on September 3, 1925, that the mighty United States dirigible *Shenandoah* flew into a line squall over Caldwell, Ohio, leaving fourteen dead on the ground and an object lesson for men who flirt with thunderstorms even at low altitudes. On October 4, 1930, the British dirigible R101 went down in a squall line over France, killing forty-six of the fifty-four persons on board. Thus as thunderstorms stopped the advance and success of the mighty lighter-than-air behemoth, they also left a series of lessons for all pilots who fly aircraft into thunderstorms.

A Case for Weather Radar

4

Too INFREQUENT are the occasions when an airliner is sucked into the maw of a violent summer thunderstorm and escapes with its life.

Yet this happened in 1941, when a Pennsylvania Central DC-3, en route from Detroit to Chicago, with an intermediate stop at Grand Rapids, Michigan, tangled with a squall line similar to the one which Captain Linn and his DC-4 encountered.

The DC-3 flew into the storm at night. The ominous presence of the anvil was indicated by a brilliant display of electrical pyrotechnics that laced the sky for almost the entire length of the lake. The air was hot, humid and unstable and storms had been predicted all that day. The DC-3 had been airborne only a few minutes, when some of the fifteen passengers and stewardess Shirley Tope saw the lightning flashes far to the west. The flight crew would also be aware of the lightning as they steered by the compass for the city of Grand Rapids, located halfway across the state and some distance north of a line from Detroit to Chicago.

One of the passengers, John Colombo, sat near the rear of the 21-passenger plane on the left-hand side. He didn't take particular notice of the tremendous lightning display to the west until after the aircraft had landed at Grand Rapids and taken off again, this time for Chicago.

As is usual and predictable in the unstable weather ahead of a thunderstorm, the plane began to rear up and then sink with a stomach-turning motion, similar to a light boat caught in the swells of a large body of water. Sharp and severe bumpiness began to shake the aircraft and the light came on: Do Not Smoke . . . Fasten Your Seat Belts.

Colombo fastened his belt and hoped the pilot would not steer into the storm.

The lightning became more blinding and more frequent. Long brilliant fingers of fire, shaped like the branches of a giant tree, reached out to illuminate the cloud banks for hundreds of miles. Several passengers, concerned with the increasing turbulence and the awesome display ahead of them, asked Miss Tope if the pilot was intending to fly into the storm. Holding on to the back of each seat as she made her way warily up the center of the passenger cabin, Miss Tope reached the flight deck and asked the captain his plans, as the passengers were complaining about the roughness and some were downright frightened.

The crew assured the stewardess that they had no intention of flying into the thunderstorm and that they would attempt to circumnavigate it in some manner. Miss Tope immediately went from seat to seat, at the risk of being severely injured, and assured the passengers that the captain was going to fly around the storm. If the passengers were reassured they certainly didn't show it. They pressed their heads to the square windows of the DC-3 and with their eyes bulging into the darkness, stared at the lightning and the tremendous cloud banks that were moving closer and closer and towering higher and higher by the minute. The DC-3 was purring along effortlessly, its speed cut from 175 miles an hour to 140 because of the bumpiness of the air.

"I could see a small city below us and then the reflection of its lights on the water and I knew we were over Lake Michigan," said passenger Colombo. "The turbulence became most violent and the plane rocked up and down like a rocking horse and swayed from side to side so wildly, I thought the tail would

come off. I felt the plane turn sharply to the left and soon we
were flying south, parallel to the shore. We flew south all the
way to Gary, Indiana, trying to get around to Chicago. But it
was no use. The storm extended far south over Indiana and
Illinois, and we turned back. At least this move was partly
reassuring, but not for long. The turbulence became even more
severe and I was frankly fearing for my life. There was only
light rain because I could clearly see towns to the east, but you
could hear the howl of the gusts over the engines, and the
updrafts and downdrafts came every few seconds. I knew they
were fighting hard in the cockpit.

"I looked around and saw our stewardess seated in the rear
seat, her safety belt fastened. She gave me a wink and a sheep-
ish little grin. I could tell she wasn't feeling too good either,
and was unable to leave her seat to aid some of the passengers
who had been calling for her. A number were quite ill. It would
have been nice to see the lights of an airport at this moment. I
am sure our captain would have made a dash for it.

"Now we were enveloped in lightning. Where it had been on
the lake side for so long, it now began to flash east of us, then
north, then south. We were completely surrounded by the
blinding flashes and the turbulence shook us unmercifully. We
were at 4,000-feet altitude. We flew on and on, droning forever, sickened by the continued bumpiness until we reached
Muskegon, far up on Lake Michigan. Then the plane made a
left-hand turn and headed west. I said to myself: the captain
has found an opening and is going around the main storm,
apparently intending to cross Lake Michigan to the western
side above Milwaukee and thence down to Chicago behind the
storm. At least he was trying to get us to our destination,
although I would have been just as glad to get back to Detroit.

"But strangely enough, the storm still seemed on every side
of us and the turbulence had not abated. My stomach was as
tight as a drum. Cold sweat coated my forehead. A good stiff
slug of whiskey would have been welcome. I suddenly heard
the engines quiet to a slow hum and the plane slowed down.
You could actually hear the shrieking wind outside. I had the

feeling we had ceased all forward motion. I knew we hadn't, but it felt that way.

"Right after the engines quietened out, the plane began to lift its nose, up, up, up. I was looking straight up at the nose. Miss Tope who sat in the rear seat was actually below me. I heard screams. The plane reared up and shook itself like a thing possessed and then flopped over on its back. I dangled upside down from my seat belt. The lights went out. Screams and shouts split the air. The plane shook and bounced completely out of control. I heard the stewardess scream. Coffee urns came crashing by. The plane rolled and I described a full arc in my belt and then I was back in my seat. The plane was righted again. The lights flickered on. I looked back. Miss Tope lay on the floor in the middle of the aisle, her eyes were closed and I couldn't tell if she was alive or dead. I tried to get up to go to her, but a tremendous updraft slammed me back into the seat. More were to follow.

"I looked around again and Miss Tope was still on the floor, her body rolling with the rolling of the aircraft. Her safety belt was shredded. She had been torn from her seat by the whiplash. My eyes traveled upwards and there on the ceiling above the aisle was a huge dent—the dent caused by the stewardess being hurled into the roof of the passenger compartment when the DC-3 looped the loop.

"I didn't know it at the time, but our pretty Miss Tope had a broken back. The diving, yawing plane didn't help it any and I was numbly wondering when it was all going to end. How soon would we hit the water? How quick would death be? Could I swim to shore? Where were we? Which emergency window would I try to get out? How would I get Miss Tope out? All these questions raced through my tortured mind.

"Another resounding downdraft and the plane reared and struggled against the overpowering grip of the storm, its fury increasing by the minute. The DC-3 was now acting like a roller coaster . . . up and down . . . sideways . . . now like a bucking bronco. Miss Tope was still quiet. But I could hear the roar of the rain on the wings and fuselage.

"Suddenly, I felt the plane dive under power. It seemed to have shaken off the storm for a moment, although we were still rocking like a light boat in an open sea. Then I saw lights underneath. They were white lights, like they came from houses. Then some red lights flickered through the rain and the way we were coming down, I knew we were either trying to land in a field or those red lights meant some airport was near. More red lights flashed under us. The ground was very close. I could see puddles in the lightning flashes. The power of the two engines was reduced and we were gliding. I could see the shining wires of a fence. Then some airport buildings loomed through the rain showers. Then we were on the ground, merciful, beautiful, cool wet earth. Everyone gave a big sigh of relief. Some of them returned to their vomit bottles.

"As soon as I got my strap undone I went to the stewardess. She lay very still, quite unconscious. A lot of confusion followed as everyone tried to get out. An ambulance arrived and rushed Miss Tope away. I asked a bewildered ramp attendant where we were. 'Traverse City,' he said. That meant we were way up the coast of Michigan, hundreds of miles off our track.

"I saw our pilot leaning against the plane, near the passenger loading platform. He was speechless for several minutes. When he regained his composure he told me that the aircraft had been taken entirely out of his control. The motions of his wheel were useless. The DC-3 was completely at the mercy of the thunderstorm. None of his controls would respond.

" 'How long were we flying out of control?' I asked him.

" 'Damn near all the time we were in the storm,' he said. 'Neither myself nor my co-pilot could hold the wheel. We flew where the storm took us. It was nice to see an airport show up underneath, believe you me.'

"I heard later that Miss Tope's father, a prominent Chicago surgeon, rushed to Traverse City and performed operations that saved her life. The whole thing was an experience I never want to go through again. Every time I hear of a plane tangling with a thunderstorm I shudder. I feel sorry for the passengers and for the crew."

•   •   •

This flight of a DC-3 into a raging thunderstorm, so graphically recalled by passenger Colombo, is important to the narrative for two reasons: It is an eyewitness account and it reveals what can happen to a plane of this type. Since speed and turbulence are the essential ingredients for breaking up an aircraft, and since the DC-3 was moving at a speed of hardly more than 130 miles an hour, how much more violent the cells of the anvil when a modern high-speed thin-winged jet or a turboprop airliner slams into the turbulence, sometimes so rapidly there isn't time to reduce speed. Good pilots, of course, will always reduce speed when entering a turbulent area. But there are cases on record where top-line commercial pilots have flown into thunderstorms without realizing that the fearsome mature cells were right in their flight path. This can sometimes be explained by the fact that on hazy summer days or in the late days of spring, banks of fluffy cumulus clouds and wisps of vapor in the humid, unstable skies often mask the dangers ahead. This is when accurate weather prediction and radar scanning are imperative.

On the perfectly lovely afternoon of May 12, 1959, the radar on Capital Airlines *Viscount* Flight 75 from New York to Atlanta was not operating. It was out of order. This is not to imply that if the aircraft had had its radar working the events which befell would not have occurred. Radar is an excellent navigational aid and can be used by knowledgeable pilots to avoid the extreme turbulence found in thunderstorms. It can locate hail and tornadoes as well. But *Viscount* Flight 75 was flying on the world's busiest air corridor, between New York and Washington, in sight of a dozen airports and a number of large cities where weather bureaus and airport personnel could see and evaluate the storms and pass along the information to every aircraft in the vicinity. Hundreds of aircraft fly in these jammed corridors day and night, and provide another source of up-to-the-minute weather observations ready to be passed along to the ground stations and to other planes.

With all these factors taken into consideration, Flight 75 makes an interesting case history.

The aircraft had departed from Detroit's Willow Run Airport at 12:40 P.M. that day and, as Flight 220, proceeded directly to La Guardia Field in New York City. After a short time on the ground, the plane would operate as Flight 75 to Atlanta. It was scheduled to depart at four o'clock.

The pilot of the aircraft was Captain William Clyde Paddack, fifty-three years old, a veteran with twenty-four years of flying behind him. He was a famous "million miler" with 22,000 flying hours to his credit. His valid airman's certificate showed he had a multiple engine rating with DC-3's, DC-4's, Lockheed *Constellations* and Vickers *Viscounts*.

His co-pilot for the trip was Michael J. Flahaven, twenty-seven, a pilot with a total of 4,000 flying hours, over half of which had been amassed in *Viscount* turboprop aircraft.

Between the two segments of their long flight, Capt. Paddack and his co-pilot visited the La Guardia Meteorological ("Met") Office, checked the weather along the projected route, talked with Air Traffic Control, and were assigned a cruising altitude of 16,000 feet. They then conferred with Capital's maintenance group about a high-pressure fuel pump and a fuel control unit that were being changed in one of the engines.

As the time for departure neared, Capt. Paddack and Flahaven left the operations room and walked out into the brilliant sunshine where the *Viscount* stood, silvery and alone. Paddack walked around the aircraft giving it his regular visual check. He looked up at the rudder and the V-tail, let his eye travel over the fuselage and the wings, looking for any signs of trouble. His eyes traveled over the engines, which stood far out from the leading edges of the sleek, thin wings that appeared incapable of supporting their weight.

Paddack then went aboard the *Viscount*, grinning and exchanging a few pleasantries with the two stewardesses for the flight—Sue Ann Wessell and Doris Gulik. At approximately 3:45 P.M., the passengers began to trickle from the terminal and within five minutes all twenty-seven of them were aboard. The noise of seat belts snapping shut added to the last-minute bustling of passengers getting the seat locations which they preferred. There was plenty of room. The *Viscount* was a 44-passenger airliner.

As the time for departure neared, Capt. Paddack questioned the weight of his aircraft because of the restriction imposed on using Runway 22, the runway to be used for his take-off. Because of the humidity and the heavy load, Capt. Paddack obviously thought he might have too much weight for the active runway, which was the shortest at the field, and he was concerned as to whether or not to siphon off some of the fuel. This is routine. It was unusually hot and humid and Paddack asked for the temperature because of the critical importance of the relationships between temperature, humidity, wind, take-off speed, and gross weight of the aircraft. Paddack was not satisfied until a senior operations agent of Capital came aboard and rechecked the computations. Only then, did he clear his aircraft for take-off procedures. Paddack was a very careful pilot.

Both pilots now looked out of their narrow windows to ensure that the ground fire extinguishers were in place, made sure the red lines on the propeller blades and spinners were aligned, and then began the final check-out of the instruments:

```
Engines synchronizer ........................Off
Instrument Master Switch ....................Off
Accumulator Master Switch ..................Off
Low Pressure Cocks ......................Open
Throttle ........................... Fully Closed
Fuel Level ........................Full Decrease
Propeller Fine Pitch Control .......Amber Light On
Flowmeter By-pass ....Switch On ......Light Out
Fuel Heaters ......Off ........Warning Light Out
Starter Master Switch ...................At Start
Booster Pumps ....................Switches On
Igniter Test Switch .....................Normal
Starter Selector ...................Engine Three
```

The cockpit check-out completed, Capt. Paddack made sure the engine selector switch was on number three and pushed the button below it. The familiar jet whine grew in intensity and after an interval of two seconds as the revolutions of the engine reached their required speed of 3500 rpm's, Capt. Paddack moved the fuel cocks open and the engine was alight. There was a *whump* and a blast of smoke spewed from the exhaust as the bonfires took over the burning of the kerosene.

Capt. Paddack then turned the selector switch to numbers four, one, and two, in that order, and the *Viscount* came fully alive. The ground crews held their hands over their ears to close out the ear-splitting whine of the mighty Rolls-Royce Dart 510 1,600-horsepower engines, each producing an additional 375 pounds of thrust from the noisy jet exhausts.

Capt. Paddack moved the four throttle levers forward. This increased the fuel to the engines and at the same time changed the pitch of the propellers to bite greater amounts of air and hurl the mass rearward over the thin wings. As the plane moved quickly away from the terminal ramp a few people waved handkerchiefs in farewell.

The aircraft whined its way to the northeast end of the La Guardia Airport. Its 60,507 pounds, just 103 pounds less than the maximum allowable for this take-off, pressed downward on the four protesting tires of the undercarriage and the tires of the long stiltlike nose-wheel assembly. The thin wings of the *Viscount* contained 14,500 pounds of kerosene and 60 gallons of water/methanol. The latter mixture was used for take-offs in soggy hot weather to give a quicker heat response from the engines in the critical final seconds during which the heavy aircraft struggled to become airborne.

Capt. Paddack lined his *Viscount* up with Runway 22 and received clearance from the La Guardia tower for take-off. He moved all four throttle levers full forward and gripped the wheel as the sleek turboprop leaped ahead, the engines roaring to life with a high-pitched scream. When the aircraft reached 108 knots, Paddack lifted her easily into the wind and pulled back on the column until his indicator showed that he was climbing at 1,000 feet per minute. The *Viscount* zoomed upward like a soaring bird, leaving a faint brown trail of unburned hydrocarbons in the air over the southwest end of the airport.

While the passengers enjoyed the breathtaking view from the large oval windows of the *Viscount*, the aircraft headed steadily upward, climbing effortlessly over the apartments and houses of Queens, over the Triborough Bridge, up over the fabulous panorama of Manhattan and into the hazy warmth of the skies over New Jersey and beyond. In fourteen minutes the flight was almost to its cruising height, when Air Traffic Control radioed Capt. Paddack that his cruising altitude had been changed to 14,000 feet instead of the original 16,000 feet, because of other traffic at that height. Paddack eased his control column forward, reduced his power, and the *Viscount* settled down to a quiet comfortable hum, the kind of gentle purring that makes *Viscount*-flying a vibrationless delight. Beneath the plane were a few scattered cumulus clouds: powder puffs on a hazy sea of greenery.

For the next forty minutes, the flight made its routine position reports. At 5 P.M. it passed over Westchester, Pennsylvania. Two minutes later, it reported that it was holding at 14,000 feet and estimated the next routine check point, Westminster, Maryland, at seventeen minutes after the hour to be followed by the next reporting point, Herndon, West Virginia.

The flight had just reported past Westchester, when the following radio transmission was received from it by the busy Washington Air Traffic Control center: ". . . ah, we've got a pretty good string of thunderstorms along that course . . . ah, if we could stay in the clear and stay a little bit south of Westminster, is that okay with you?"

"Capital Seventy-five . . . that will be all right, and report passing Westminster," replied the Washington Air Traffic Control.

The flight acknowledged this message and seven minutes later again contacted Washington with the following transmission: "Ah . . . Washington Center. . . . This is Capital Seventy-five, we've reduced to one seven zero knots account of rough air."

This was the last message from the flight. It indicated that Capt. Paddack was in turbulence associated with the thunderstorms predicted along his route. He had reduced the forward speed of his *Viscount* considerably, a sure sign that he was in heavy turbulence.

The fact that thunderstorms should be encountered on his flight path must not have surprised Capt. Paddack. His weather briefing at La Guardia would have shown them. Meteorological warnings had been issued continuously that day to all airport weather offices on the Eastern Seaboard indicating that a dangerous storm front could be expected. At the time that Paddack and his *Viscount* entered the turbulence, a predicted cold front had existed along a line from Philadelphia to Baltimore, swinging slightly westward at the south end toward Gordonsville, Virginia.

Regional weather forecasts issued by the Washington Weather Bureau at seven o'clock on that morning of May 12, 1959, and again at one o'clock, had drawn attention to the possibility of severe thunderstorms and extreme turbulence associated with the almost stationary cold front. The Weather Bureau at Idlewild Airport, New York, had issued a similar warning to all aircraft pilots at 2 P.M. that afternoon, stressing the possibility of severe storms and a good chance of a violent squall line in advance of this frontal system.

Capt. Paddack knew this.

At 2:15 P.M., as if the other warnings were not enough (and it seems they never are) Idlewild issued a special flash advisory. Capt. Paddack and his co-pilot should have been made aware of this as soon as they checked the weather for their Southern flight. A flash advisory customarily deals with hazardous weather expected within a period of two to four hours from the time it is issued. It automatically amends all other area forecasts, even when potentially dangerous weather has already been adequately forecast.

A flash advisory usually means danger, and most pilots treat it with respect. This one read: "Line of scattered thunderstorm activity, near Martinsburg-Harrisburg-Poughkeepsie north-eastward, is moving eastward about 20 knots, accompanied by severe turbulence, and the conditions below 1,000 feet, visibility two miles. This line will move to near Providence, New York City, and Philadelphia by six o'clock, increasing in intensity during the afternoon. This report is valid to 6:15 P.M."

As soon as this report was issued, Capital Airlines operations at Washington's National Airport received the alert. The areas involved by the gathering storm were marked off on a black-board chart on the wall of the flight dispatch office, so that all Capital pilots operating out of Washington would be aware of the severe weather warning. It indicated that Capital Airlines officials in Washington knew of the danger and were in a position to so advise any of their flights penetrating the storm areas.

During this same afternoon, radar storm reports were gathered and issued almost every hour by Andrews Air Force Base, near Washington, describing the movement of this line of thunderstorms. These reports were also issued on Capital Airlines' teletype machines to all flight dispatch offices on the Eastern Seaboard.

All this tends to indicate that the Federal Weather Bureaus were, as usual, on their toes, and that all possible flying agencies were advised of the danger in the warm afternoon skies. I myself was flying that afternoon in a *Viscount* from Detroit to Washington. The tremendous storm build-up could be seen for many miles. As the plane approached the Harrisburg-Gettysburg area, it turned to the south and then spiraled down over the green fields of Virginia before making the final approach to the capital's National Airport. This storm was very black and towered to tremendous heights. The anvil was not clear. There were considerable numbers of powder-puff clouds, typical of the clouds that follow the course of a cold front.

At 3:48 P.M., this cold front moved ponderously across the Baltimore area, lashing the city and the surrounding countryside with black sheets of rain, stabbed by vicious bolts of forked lightning. There was a pronounced change in the wind direction and gusts along the leading edge of the front roared up to sixty miles an hour. A severe temperature drop followed as the frontal system moved through the city. Not far away, at Martin Airport—the private airport serving the aerospace industrial complex—large thunderstorms appeared to be in the process of mature development, and extreme turbulence was said to exist in the upper levels, particularly at 14,000 feet. And Martin Airport was just two and a half miles from the last reported position of Flight 75.

When Capt. Paddack sent his last message he was just 2,500 yards from violence.

There is evidence that Paddack was not kept fully informed of the developing thunderstorms by his own people, and it was believed that he turned from the mass of thunderheads and flew for a short time parallel to the cold front. Then, seeing what he believed was an opening, he turned and entered a particularly active cell.

Another airline pilot, operating in approximately the same area and at the same time as Flight 75, flew into the turbulence, turned around and flew out again. This seems a sensible act, although a great many pilots will not attempt to bank their planes when they have once entered turbulence for fear of losing control. At the same time, not far from the scene of Paddack's last reported position, an executive aircraft pilot reported that he was just a little north of Paddack's flight and traveling the same direction, when he observed in his radar screen a severe thunderstorm cell. He described it as "twice as strong as any others in the area."

Remember that Paddack's radar was not operating.

At 4:10 P.M., the *Viscount* reached the seething thunderstorm cell, a cell that contained the kind of turbulence that can take a plane out of the control of human hands and whirl it like a toy.

The Vickers *Viscount* is an exceptionally rugged aircraft. Built by Vickers-Armstrong at Weybridge, England, it made its first flights in 1948 and was introduced into North American service in 1954 by Trans-Canada Air Lines. This introduction was followed closely by Capital Airlines which purchased the British planes to launch itself into the highly competitive U. S. domestic service.

One airline executive once described the *Viscount* as "the world's worst airplane with the world's finest engines."

He was, of course, referring to the appearance of the ship. It was never a pretty airplane, and the flight deck looked like it had been added as an afterthought. But it was quiet and comfortable and its four Rolls-Royce Dart engines were masterpieces of engine construction. They just never wore out. With the exception of a broken bolt in a flap, which caused a fatal crash in England; and a runaway propeller which caused a single fatality in the skies over Michigan, the *Viscount* chalked up an impressive record of safety and reliability. It had, however, a tendency to yaw in extreme turbulence.

There were more than 100 witnesses to what took place in the last moments of Capt. Paddack's aircraft, and most of them agreed that the *Viscount* came apart in the air at between 3,000 and 7,000 feet. Apparently, Paddack lost control of his aircraft at the 14,000-foot level and then struggled to regain control as the aircraft screamed downward at 3,000 feet per minute, losing its wings when it reached the 5,200-foot level.

When the wings shattered, the kerosene tanks immediately ruptured and a tremendous explosion and fire followed. Yet the crew and the twenty-seven passengers aboard were not to be spared the next spine-chilling seconds. They were all to live until they hit the soft wet mud of a Maryland swamp, and the soggy marsh in several shallow inlets of Chesapeake Bay, in an area approximately two miles northeast of Chase, Maryland.

Herman Altenberg, who operates a farm in this district, was working with his son in the field when a stab of lightning interrupted his labors. Both turned southwestward, perceived the blackness of the storm moving toward them, and immediately ran toward the farmhouse. The rain caught up with them and they sprinted for the homestead through the noisy clatter of

This first Vickers Viscount, shown here over Montreal, Canada, ushered in turboprop service in North America. It brought to the air-traveling public new quietness in flight, faster schedules, and expansive windows for breath-taking views. (Photo by the author)

the huge raindrops. But they did not reach their destination. Something in the twisting turbulent sky above them caught their attention. It was a ball of fire. It wasn't lightning, of that they were sure. They described it as a bonfire in the sky, growing larger by the second and coming downward at a great rate of speed.

From the ball of fire, debris was falling, and the entire clutter fell to the earth about a mile away, although both father and son thought the fire was going to descend right on top of them. They were badly shaken by the experience.

At the same time, John Hammen, a district telephone lineman, was driving along a country road near Chase when he saw the ball of fire and the debris slam into the earth. He jumped from his car, ran to the nearest telephone pole, quickly climbed it, tapped the wires, and notified police of the incident. Then he called ambulances and doctors to the scene.

Capt. Paddack, First Officer Flahaven, two pretty stewardesses, and the twenty-seven passengers were dead—spread grotesquely over several square miles of Maryland countryside. The tragedy was the second within the hour for Capital Airlines. Two persons were killed and six were injured when a *Super Constellation* landed in the same bad weather but behind the storm, at the airport at Charleston, West Virginia. The huge aircraft, with forty passengers aboard, skidded along the wet runway in heavy rain and then went over the end, plummeting down a 200-foot embankment before coming to a crunching stop. Luckily, it didn't explode.

Investigation of the Maryland disaster by the highly efficient Civil Aeronautics Board revealed that the *Viscount* had made an "involuntary" descent from 14,000 feet to the surface of the ground. In simple terms, this means that the pilot had not deliberately brought the plane to a lower altitude. The downdrafts of the storm alone had accomplished the task. The board arrived at this conclusion because evidence revealed that the plane's flaps were up and so was the landing gear. Eyewitness reports also indicated, beyond a shadow of a doubt, that the plane had broken up in the air, and this breakup had been followed by explosion of the fuel. The aircraft had come apart because it was twisted and tossed well beyond its design strength.

With the help of the Army and several civil organizations, the investigating board was able to recover about 90 per cent of the aircraft structure and it was moved to a nearby hangar, laid out, and given meticulous examination. Every twisted scrap of metal, every fire-blackened engine part, every item of the intricate control system, radio, seats, lights, and cables was moved into its rightful place like a giant jigsaw puzzle. Despite the widely scattered fragments and the damage caused by the explosion and fire, and despite the theft of parts by scavengers, the CAB probers were able to pinpoint the probable cause.

Both wings had separated in flight, indicating the tremendous and fantastic forces that were at work to cause a failure of this kind. The horizontal stabilizers had failed also. The vertical fin was wrenched away, taking part of the fuselage with it.

The fuselage of the *Viscount* had snapped into three pieces after the explosion. The flight deck and the forward part of the passenger cabin, forward of the wings, stayed together for the fatal plunge earthward. The center part of the passenger cabin over the wings broke away from the rest and fell with fire pouring from its anguished metal. The aft section, taking the last four seats of the aircraft and the lavatories, galley and tail section, traveled its own flight path to the ground. All three sections, with hundreds of flaming bits of scrap, descended over an area of two and a half miles.

The CAB investigators could find no evidence that the aircraft had been struck by lightning. There was no indication that a fire and explosion had occurred before the structural breakup. Investigation was to reveal clearly that when the left wing separated from the plunging *Viscount,* the fuel tanks on the left side were ripped open and there had been an instantaneous fire of great intensity. This left wing had fallen to the ground some distance to the rear of the wreckage and was burned to almost unrecognizable ash.

All four Rolls-Royce Dart turboprop engines had separated from their attaching structures at the time of the general breakup. These separations were caused by fierce uploads, although evidence revealed that violent downloads had occurred just seconds prior.

A check of the instruments disclosed to the CAB that the *Viscount* had been traveling at a forward speed of 170 knots, which was the recommended rough air penetration for a *Viscount*. Capt. Paddack had been following the procedures according to the book.

Examination of all the passenger seats, with the exception of one that was never found and which might have been carted away by a souvenir hunter, revealed that they had been subjected to tremendous loads and had been torn from their anchorages in the floor before the aircraft began to come apart. One can only imagine the appalling conditions within the plane as all the seats broke loose and went flying back and forth with their human loads, up and down, within the diving, careening aircraft.

The state of Maryland requires that autopsies be performed upon all victims of a plane crash and this law was dutifully carried out.

The medical examinations disclosed that most of the injuries sustained by the passengers occurred before the *Viscount* struck the ground. Various injuries on heads and shoulders revealed that passengers suffered them by striking the roof and sides of the passenger compartment. Nearly all the injuries were head bumps and scalp lacerations, but none were of sufficient force to cause death, perhaps unfortunately.

Of the twenty-seven passengers, medical examination revealed that twenty of them were badly mauled and painfully injured before the aircraft disintegrated. Some of these had seat-belt injuries, caused when squeezed by tremendous G forces into their safety belts. Others had been burned by the hot flames of the burning kerosene. But none had been struck by lightning. And all had expired instantly on striking the ground.

After the painstaking investigation of the *Viscount* disaster the Civil Aeronautics Board came to the following conclusion.

"The Board fully recognizes that there are many factors in adverse weather phenomena that are difficult to assess accurately. The Board has therefore advocated every practical assistance to pilots transporting the public. The Board believes that aircraft radar has proved to be such an assistance, particularly in modern high-performance aircraft.

"While it is impossible to predict precisely the action which would have been taken by the captain had the airborne radar been operable, there is evidence to indicate the likelihood that the area of turbulence could have been avoided through the use of airborne radar.

"The Board therefore concludes, that the provision of airborne radar on such aircraft would enhance aviation safety," the official report stated. Since 1960 the Federal Aviation Authority has required airborne radar on all jet aircraft.

Thus ends a story of a modern airliner's contact with a typical afternoon thunderstorm in an area where weather reports were up to date and efficient, and warnings had been issued over a prolonged period of time.

Two Pawns in the Elements

5

AFTER WORLD WAR II, there was a mad scramble of the airlines of the United States and the government-owned and government-controlled airlines of Canada, Britain, France, Holland, and many others to find a suitable long-range, money-making transport for the promising transatlantic business.

Giant airframe manufacturers in the U. S., like Douglas, Boeing, and Lockheed, worked overtime to get their long-range concepts off the drafting boards and into prototypes, all the while pressuring engine manufacturers, such as Pratt & Whitney and Curtiss-Wright, to come up with greater horsepower and modest fuel consumption. Transatlantic passengers were the prize in a competition between private airlines, government airlines and fly-by-nights. Money could be made from the Goliaths of the sky—Boeing's *Stratocruiser,* Lockheed's *Constellation,* Douglas's DC-6.

All these fine long-range transports appeared to be acceptable to almost everyone, with one or two exceptions. The main exception was Canada.

The publicly owned Trans-Canada Air Lines badly needed a four-engine transport for the vast distances of its domestic routes as well as for the North Atlantic. The U. S. designs looked good. But to cool the pro-British political fires which constantly burn in the Dominion, Trans-Canada looked for an all-Canadian plane or an all-British plane, or a combination of Commonwealth fuselage and power plants that would please Canadian passengers.

As a result, a bastard was born.

Trans-Canada Air Lines and the Canadian Department of Transport put their heads together and came up with an aircraft that would please the government. Apparently no one considered the airline passengers. The plane would be partly U. S. and partly British.

The group decided that the airliner would have the fuselage of the Douglas DC-6 and the engines of Rolls-Royce. Since the DC-6 was not yet in production, Trans-Canada decided on a lengthened body of the DC-4 with squared windows which would be several feet shorter than the coming DC-6. They would call it the DC-4M-2.

Canadair at Montreal, a division of General Dynamics, was picked to build the aircraft. It would be powered by four Rolls-Royce Merlin engines, the same Merlins which won fame in the Battle of Britain by powering the Vickers Supermarine *Spitfires* and then went on to even greater fame by powering the mighty *Lancaster* bombers.

Canadair decided to name the political combination the "Canadair Four." Trans-Canada didn't like this name and decided to call the package the "North Star." British Overseas Airways Corporation, anxious to please the government with as many British-made parts as possible, liked the Canadian arrangement and placed a sizable order with Canadair. Only they would call the plane the "Argonaut."

The combination was a delightful political package. It was U. S. designed, British powered, and Canadian built.

Despite its political background, the aircraft proved to have a fairly reliable combination of ingredients. However, it had a few things against it. The engines were water cooled and often the tricky radiator flaps would close and cause overheated engines. Sometimes fire warnings would flicker as the engines cruised from one temperature band to another. There were times when the aircraft did not respond immediately to its

A Trans-Canada Air Lines North Star is seen taking off from a Canadian airport. Fully loaded, a plane of this type was caught in a violent mountain thunderstorm and impaled itself on Mount Slesse in the Canadian Rockies. (Photo by the author)

throttles and would be sluggish on take-off and slow to answer in flight.

The term "false start" became rather familiar to Trans-Canada Air Lines pilots. This referred to times when the *North Star* couldn't muster enough strength to become airborne, and the weary crew would have to route the lumbering aircraft around the airport perimeter and start the take-off all over again, sometimes having to wait in a long line-up and to request a new flight corridor before getting a second crack at the take-off.

Yet, despite these failings, the DC-4M-2 made a good showing in Canada and elsewhere, chalking up ten and twelve hours of utilization a day, when other and more famous transports were only able to get in eight and nine hours daily utilization.

The DC-4M-2 was an aircraft that made money. But it was a transport that passengers would just as soon forget. It was extremely noisy, being downright deafening during take-off and while climbing to cruising altitude. This was due to the fact that the Merlin was an inline engine with exhausts directed toward the passenger compartment. The vibration from the Merlins was stupefying. What had provided topnotch power in bombers and fighter planes was not necessarily the best for passenger transports.

To reassure its Canadian passengers, Trans-Canada Air Lines' publicity and advertising concentrated on the reliability of the plane. In turn, the public seemed to accept the well-aimed publicity. But what else could they do? They had no other transcontinental airline on which to travel. The *North Star* was their only plane and they flew in it.

But if the noisy Merlin engines assaulted the ears of the passengers, the night brought added terrors. When darkness cloaked the sky over the vast Canadian wilderness, the exhaust manifolds of the engines glowed menacingly, sending out showers of dull-red sparks into the void behind. When the pilot would change from climbing power, the exhausts would change their color from a brilliant orange to a dull red and remain that way until the power was reduced for landing. Then they would change to a faint blood-red glow.

Not even the most hardened air traveler likes to peer out his window at night and see red-hot exhausts belching from the engines and trailing hot gases back over wings in which are stored thousands of gallons of high-octane gasoline.

Yet, in the last analysis, it wasn't the night or the flaming exhausts that caused the customers to complain. It was the ear-splitting noise. Finally, Trans-Canada and Canadair were forced to modify the situation. They designed a crossover exhaust system. This system took the noisy exhaust gases from the passenger side of each engine and transferred them through a lengthened exhaust system over the engine and out the other side. This helped choke off some of the sound and also managed to hide the hot exhausts and the flaming trails.

The noise level dropped drastically. Had it not done so, there was a good chance that public complaints would have reached the ears of the Canadian Parliament. During all the fuss, the Royal Canadian Air Force accepted the *North Star* as a military transport—which is what it should have been right from the start.

On March 2, 1949, a DC-4M-2 moved from the assembly line of Canadair into the sunlight. Workmen affixed four giant blue letters BOAC on the fuselage. The registration on the wings and tail was G-ALHE.

Equipped to carry forty passengers in two cabins—twenty-four in the front cabin and sixteen in the rear—it was a roomy plane. Its wide foam rubber seats faced forward, with the exception of four seats at the very front of the forward cabin and the four front seats of the aft cabin. These faced rearward. There were four emergency exits in the front cabin, two on either side, and two exits in the rear section, one on either side of the cabin. These exits were merely enlarged window frames and could be quickly removed in time of trouble.

After its airworthiness tests, this particular *Argonaut* took off from Montreal and flew to London, where it was immediately pressed into the world-wide service of British Overseas Airways Corporation (BOAC). By June of 1956, more than seven years later, this same *Argonaut* had amassed an impressive total of 18,000 hours of service. On June 13, its certificate of air worthiness was reissued by the British Air Ministry and it continued at its never-ending work, shuttling along the busy African routes between Lagos, Nigeria, and London, England.

On June 22, 1956, just nine days after receiving this air worthiness certificate, the old G-ALHE landed at Rome because of trouble in the number-two engine (the power plant located adjacent to the passenger compartment on the left side of the aircraft). The Merlin engine was replaced, and the aircraft then continued on its regular run to the south.

After such an impressive record with its original Merlin engines, it was most unfortunate that the new engine in the number-two position would not be able to join the illustrious ranks of the three others.

In exactly nineteen hours the plane would be a blackened, unrecognizable heap of junk.

The scene of the disaster would be Kano, the bustling city of the north-central Nigerian plateau. Kano is 500 miles inland from the Gulf of Guinea, in the middle of the hot, dry tropical zone of the African continent.

The *Argonaut* had worked its way south to Lagos, the port of Nigeria, and on June 24, 1956, started back on its return flight to London with scheduled stops at Kano and Tripoli. The first lap was the 550-mile jump from Lagos to Kano and this was completed uneventfully at 6:40 P.M.

The crew of five officers and three cabin attendants, who would take the plane on to Tripoli and London, had arrived at the airport forty minutes earlier. They had flown into Kano the night before and had rested for some twenty-three hours. During their period of enforced waiting, the crew members had visited bazaars that offered wares brought along one of the oldest caravan routes in Africa. At one time, Kano was the center of the thriving African slave trade. Traces of the old slave compounds were still visible.

Lean and tan and looking his thirty-six years, Captain H. V. Tomlinson, veteran pilot of the Royal Air Force, headed the flight crew, which included First Officer John Slatford, thirty-one; Navigation Officer C. F. Young, thirty-three; and Radio Officer H. E. Hoare, forty-four. There were two stewards for the flight, L. A. Ward and G. H. Langton, and one stewardess, Kay Buckley.

While awaiting the arrival of the flight from Lagos, Capt. Tomlinson and First Officer Slatford checked in with BOAC operations. Then they studied the weather reports over the 1,400-mile route which would take them over the world's most forbidding land: the trackless wastes of the Sahara and Libyan Deserts, where there were no emergency landing fields, and where aircraft had been known to disappear without a trace.

The flight from Kano to Tripoli was a journey that always gave even the toughest pilots a twinge of worry. It was long, lonely, and mysterious, with no beacons or radio towers to guide the way, and much depended on experienced navigators like Young, who had traveled over difficult routes since 1947.

Captain Tomlinson himself had flown this route on many occasions during his 15 years of flying which had begun when he joined the RAF back in 1941. In the war he had flown bombers over Germany. They were *Lancasters* with Merlin engines. This had given him many thousands of hours' experience with these particular power plants. When the air raids ceased, he had joined BOAC in 1945 and piloted DC-3's and *Yorks* until 1949 when he became a first officer on the newly-arrived *Argonaut*. He remained with this type of aircraft chalking up 4,203 hours, of which 603 hours were as pilot-in-command, as the British say.

All this indicated that Capt. Tomlinson was a man who knew his aircraft, and in fact so did Slatford, his co-pilot. The latter, a pilot with the Royal Air Force from 1942 until 1947, had collected more than 1,500 hours before joining BOAC. His total flying experience was 3,733 hours, of which more than half had been at the controls of the *Argonaut*.

When the two men arrived at Kano Airport on this June evening, the weather was partly cloudy and the temperature was 94 degrees, quite comfortable in this high-plateau country.

Cumulus clouds formed a fairly heavy pattern above 3,500 feet and helped to shade the hot, dry earth below. A slight wind blew from the northwest. All this they noted as they walked to the terminal.

Tomlinson and Slatford were informed of the general weather picture for the entire northern Nigerian region. Typical of this time of year, there was a moist southwesterly air current of southerly origin some 10,000 feet in depth lying over northern Nigeria, and above this mass was a dry easterly air current which had originated in the north. The combined air mass was unstable and there were several isolated thunderstorms in the Kano region. About 400 miles to the east, a line squall was gathering momentum as it moved westward, but was not expected to reach Kano until the next day.

Except for those scattered thunderstorms, everything seemed clear for the long haul to Tripoli.

As usual, the arriving *Argonaut* could be heard long before it came into sight. When the plane landed, it was immediately refueled while BOAC checked in the passengers. There would be a total of thirty-eight for the flight.

Captain Tomlinson was concerned about the threat of thunderstorms as he stood outside the operations building and searched the skies around him. It was reasonably clear over the airport. But he could see a large thunderstorm mass some distance away to the east-northeast of the airport. Yet he could hear no thunder. His intended track to the north appeared to be clear, but to the west he could see two huge cumulus clouds and he decided to find out more about them if he could.

Buttonholing the incoming pilot of the *Argonaut*, Capt. Tomlinson asked him if he had noticed the cumulus formations west and east of the airport when he was flying toward Kano and if he had noticed any signs of lightning activity. The incoming pilot replied that he had indeed noticed that the overhang of the east-northeast storm was over the airport itself at a tremendous height above the ground and invisible from the airport because of the scattered lower clouds. The base of the first cloud layer was still 3,500 feet and the base of the second layer was 15,000 feet. The incoming pilot went on to caution Tomlinson that the east-northeast storm was moving around to the northeast and might soon infringe upon his flight path, and that the movement of this particular storm further revealed the tops of more thunderstorms to the east.

Captain Tomlinson decided at this point to consult the meteorological forecaster personally to ascertain whether there was any line squall reported near the airport and to inquire as to how fast the northeast thunderstorm was moving, and in what direction. He was taking every precaution because he had a high respect for thunderstorms.

The British Ministry of Transport and Civil Aviation continuously informed airlines and pilots of the danger of thunderstorms and had on many occasions circulated widely a white paper on the effects of thunderstorms on commercial aircraft operations.

This seven-page white paper has long been considered one of the best sources of up-to-date information in the business. It was compiled after years of research by the Royal Aircraft Establishment at Farnborough, England, and at the United Kingdom Meteorological Offices. It also contained the experiences of the United States Thunderstorm Project of 1946 to 1949.

One of the passages in the seven-page circular is of particular importance and seems particularly applicable to the situation developing at Kano. It also fits two other chapters in this book concerning jet disasters.

The passage reads: "Before take-off, make a thorough analysis of the weather situation to determine the probable location of thunderstorms. Plan the flight to avoid them. Special attention should be given to thunderstorms in the vicinity of the airfield. *If there is any risk of the aircraft flying into the influence of an active thunderstorm cell during its initial climb, it will be advisable to delay the take-off.*" [Italics added]

· · ·

Tomlinson closely studied the situation before making his decision. During his talk with the duty forecaster concerning the possibility of a line squall in the area he was assured that the squall line of danger lay some 400 miles to the east, and that the storm in the Kano district was not associated with any line squall and was purely local in development.

As it was local, the forecaster thought that it would move very little, and if it did, it would move slowly from east to west.

All of this information was reassuring to Tomlinson. He thanked the forecaster and was leaving the Met office when he bumped into his navigator, C. F. Young.

"We'll probably have to go a little way off track to the west after we take off," he said. "I want to avoid the main belt of rain from the thunderstorm which should pass about eight or ten miles north of the airport."

"How's our fuel load?" asked Young.

"Fine," Tomlinson replied. "We'll have more than one hundred gallons over what we'll need for this flight. And, by the way, I want to get off as quickly as possible."

Tomlinson returned to the BOAC operations department and informed the officer on duty that he desired to get off the ground as quickly as possible. The aircraft's documents were completed and signed at 7:07 P.M. The passengers were ordered aboard immediately.

Tomlinson walked around the *Argonaut*, making his usual visual inspection, and, while doing so, heard the rumble of distant thunder. He paused for a moment to scan the dark cloudy skies to the west and northwest. He saw another *Argonaut* landing on Runway 25, the same runway from which he would be taking off in a few minutes. He noticed that the incoming plane had made its landing approach much closer to the storm center than he would be. But since the landing appeared to be normal in every respect he believed that his impending take-off would be unhindered. He heard two more rumbles of thunder and saw lighting flashing in the main storm area but none to the west of him or close to the airport.

The thirty-eight passengers embarked and Miss Buckley checked off their names as they took their seats in the aircraft. Then she went to the rear and took her seat beside the two stewards, Ward and Langton. The engines were started with their customary Merlin roar and belching of black smoke and flame and all four were growling in unison by 7:15 P.M. One minute later, the aircraft receive taxi clearance from the Kano control tower and Tomlinson eased her along the concrete pavement to the warm-up threshold at the end of Runway 25. The tower informed him that the surface wind was at 300 degrees at 15 knots and the altimeters should be made to read 1012 millibars.

Rain began to fall. It became quite heavy, typical of all sudden tropical downpours. But the visibility remained good and Tomlinson watched for any sign which would indicate wind gusting or the presence of the roll-type cloud which is associated with the line squall of a storm. There were no such indications, although the dense black area of the cloud was now very near in the northeast.

In order to save time, most of the pre-take-off checks were made during the taxiing period and the engines were run up at the same time, so that when the aircraft reached the threshold, it was ready for take-off.

Captain Tomlinson quickly snapped on the windshield wipers. He could see the end of the runway clearly and he estimated the visibility at two miles. It was now completely overcast and raining heavily, and no clear patches could be seen. The surface wind was still 15 knots at 300 degrees.

The crew quickly completed the pre-take-off check-out and set the wing flaps at 10 degrees, centralized the trim control, and asked for take-off clearance from the tower. This was granted.

The tower controller noted in his log that the wind was now 20 knots at 270 degrees and visibility was 1,500 yards.

Tomlinson shoved the four levers of the throttles full forward, gripped the wheel tightly as the *Argonaut* gathered speed and started down the runway toward the southwest.

After an easy run of 2,000 yards, the aircraft lifted at exactly 7:21½ P.M.

During the take-off, the visibility had decreased, owing to the heavy rain on the windshield. This situation caused Tomlinson to fly by his instruments as soon as he lifted the wheels from the runway. At no time, however, did he deem the torrential rain sufficient to cause him to abort the take-off. He had previously taken off on several occasions in weather conditions that had appeared to be of a similar nature.

As soon as the *Argonaut* lifted, First Officer Slatford pulled up the lever that controlled the undercarriage. The wheels retracted within five seconds and were tucked away in the belly and in the nose. At this precise moment, the aircraft passed over the end of the runway at a height of 100 feet with an air speed of 125 knots. Shortly afterwards, Tomlinson called for the first power reduction and Slatford eased the throttles to 54 inches of manifold pressure in the four engines and then eased the propeller revolutions to a hearty 2,850 per minute. At this moment the pilots noticed a slight updraft, but the air-speed fluctuations were no greater than five knots and there was no tendency for either wing to drop. Everything appeared to be first rate.

The normal climb was made to above 240 feet, when Tomlinson called out: "Flaps up."

The air speed was now fluctuating between 125 and 130 knots and the rate of climb was 300 feet per minute.

The rain continued heavy and there appeared to be more ahead. Tomlinson noticed a gap in the rain to the west-north-west. He was now at 250 feet. The aircraft had disappeared from the view of those in the control tower.

No sink was noticed by the pilots when the flaps were retracted, although the speed dropped slightly and remained at 123 knots. Tomlinson looked at the instruments while the flaps were retracting and noted that the height was 260 to 270 feet. The *Argonaut* was level and steady and roaring noisily.

The situation remained static for a few seconds, long enough for Tomlinson and Slatford to think that the air speed should be building up, when suddenly they were horrified to see the indicated air speed dropping steadily and quickly.

"Full power," shouted Tomlinson, and Slatford immediately responded, shoving the levers full forward.

Tomlinson eased the nose downward slightly to build up his air speed, which was already down to 103 knots.

(The stalling speed of the aircraft at this moment was 97 knots with power on and 104 knots with power off.)

Slatford leaned forward and looked intently at the four engine instruments. They were all normal. He opened the throttle fully with the rpm still set at 2,850. He did not have time to increase the rpm's to their fullest, which was 3,000, because the master rpm lever of the aircraft was broken down.

The *Argonaut* was slow to respond. The full throttle did not increase the air speed, which remained steady at 103 knots. The stall warning horn was blowing steadily, an unnerving racket in the cockpit. The stall warning light was blinking steadily.

During this sudden emergency Tomlinson did not adjust the trim of the aircraft and experienced no turbulence or sinking. His sole concern was the low speed of the plane, and neither he nor Slatford had time to note what loss of height or rate of descent was being indicated on the instruments. They were too busy fighting for response from the engines and their eyes stared with utter disbelief at the dangerously low air speed.

The *Argonaut* lost height rapidly. By the time the co-pilot had fully opened the throttles and taken note of the rising manifold pressures, he looked out quickly and was startled. The aircraft was nearly at treetop height and flying in an almost-level attitude.

Meanwhile, satisfied that his plane was no longer losing air speed, Tomlinson, clearly in the worst emergency of his brilliant flying career, looked out his window and saw that he was flying level but only about fifteen or twenty feet above the ground.

There was a tree directly in his path 200 yards ahead.

Tomlinson started to bank the aircraft to the right, being careful that his right wing did not touch the ground. Then he attempted to climb by pulling back gently on the control column.

The aircraft began to respond to the controls, but the tree was now immediately in front of the aircraft and slightly to the left. Tomlinson jerked back on the control column, hoping at the last second to get above the menace. But his efforts were in vain. The underside of the nose section and the left wing of the *Argonaut* struck the tree seventeen feet above its base. The left wing opened up and the fuel tanks ruptured. Fire broke out immediately and the outer part of the left wing wrenched itself from the rest of the plane and careened 160 yards from the tree.

A second tree, 300 yards beyond the first, was then struck by the remaining portion of the left wing (known as the left wing root). The left side of the rear fuselage and the leading edge of the right rear tailplane also struck the tree. This tremendous impact caused the rear fuselage and tail unit to break away. The aircraft yawed wildly to the left and struck two more trees in rapid succession.

The forty passenger seats broke away from their supports, hurling passengers in all directions. The last two impacts with the trees caused the remaining portion of the left wing to shear off and the rear passenger cabin to wrench away, careen through the air, and then bounce along the muddy ground. The aircraft, or what was left of it, veered to the left and came apart, scattering pieces over 140 yards, while the right wing broke free and split into three sections. Explosions quickly followed and flames leaped high into the sky. Some twenty-one of the passenger seats were hurled so far from the plane they were left untouched by the mounting fires.

Capt. Tomlinson was miraculously alive. So was his co-pilot, Slatford. But the navigator lay limp in death over his shattered plotting board and Radio Officer Hoare was terribly injured. Flames engulfed the flight deck, and Tomlinson, disregarding his own safety, helped Hoare to the crew door but was unable to open it. It had jammed. With the roar of the flames becoming louder by the second, Tomlinson groped in the smoke-filled flight deck for the emergency axe so as to smash his way clear before the unruptured fuel cells exploded. But he was unable to find the axe. Then he and Slatford dragged Hoare away from the flames which were licking into the flight deck. Tomlinson managed to pry open the left cockpit window and, after shoving Slatford through it and squeezing the badly injured Hoare through the narrow opening, made good his escape.

Tomlinson was much luckier than many of the others. Of the thirty-eight passengers aboard the *Argonaut,* twenty-nine were either killed or were trapped in the flames and were dying. Pretty stewardess Kay Buckley was trapped in her seat in the rear section and was dead. Steward Ward was also killed. Steward Langdon had been thrown clear but was seriously injured.

Tomlinson and Slatford fought their way into the fire-drenched area and dragged out several screaming passengers, dragging them twenty or thirty yards upwind. They started pulling all those to safety who were nearest the spreading flames or were lying next to fuel cells which had not yet caught fire. They were able to save only nine persons before the flames took over, and of these, two were critically injured, five were seriously injured, and two were unscathed.

Meanwhile, back at the control tower, the officers on duty had watched the take-off and had seen the *Argonaut* disappear behind the black curtain of rain. A moment or so later, they saw a burst of fire in the trees in the same direction and immediately pressed the sirens, which wailed out across the field and chilled the hearts of those friends and relatives still in the BOAC waiting room.

The fire crew ran to the fire engine stationed below the tower and sped to the scene. One of the control officers raced to a rescue tender and guided all other vehicles to the crash area. All the rescue and fire vehicles proceeded at maximum speed with four-wheel drive, as the terrain was farming land and deep in mud for more than 1,000 yards. Despite the rain and the mud, they reached the scene, which was 2½ miles from Kano, in less than ten minutes and commenced putting out the fires and aiding the injured passengers and crew.

Nigerian police also rushed to the scene and with airport officers got all those injured to Kano Hospital in the quickest possible time. The degree of efficiency they demonstrated later brought them the highest praise from the British Government.

Wing Commander E. H. Coleman, A.F.C., director of civil aviation for West Africa, hurried to the disaster and with other government and technical officials carried out an intensive investigation into the crash. It was as thorough as British thoroughness can be. The result of their findings was brought before a Civil Aviation Board of Enquiry, convened on June 30, 1956, by K. Ozuomba Mbadiwe, Minister of Communications and Aviation for Nigeria.

Three other members joined Wing Commander Coleman on the Board of Enquiry, namely: Wing Commander R. P. Garnons-Williams, senior inspector of accidents for the Ministry of Transport and Civil Aviation; Captain C. B. Houlder, senior captain of BOAC; and S. H. Nicholson, operations officer of the Department of Civil Aviation.

This board heard the testimony of many witnesses to the disaster including the surviving passengers and the captain and first officer. After listening to all the eyewitness stories and studying the details of the aircraft and its engines, the question of weather arose. This was covered in great detail by the following report of the British West Africa Meteorological Services which was read into the record:

(1) *Kano weather—6 P.M. to 8 P.M. on June 24, 1956.*

At 6 P.M. there were two thunderstorms in the vicinity of Kano, one about ten miles to the northeast of the airport and the other about six miles southwest. Both were moving slowly towards the southwest and by 7 P.M. the former lay a mile or two to the northeast with an associate cloud overhang extending over the airport itself. Moderate rain from this overhang started to fall at the terminal building at 7:14 and ended at 7:22 yielding about 0.2 inches of rain in all. The main center of the thunderstorm passed a little to the north of the airport but a new cell appears to have developed in the overhang, which gave heavy rain and squalls over the western half of the airport at about 7:20 P.M. and moved westwards. The evidence of witnesses in the area south and west of the end of the runway establishes beyond a reasonable doubt that a strong easterly squall line with associated heavy rain was expected there though instrumental evidence is lacking.

(2) *Comment in Relation to the Accident*

The strong wind and heavy rain from the new cell appear to have reached the ground just as the aircraft was taking off. The surface wind from this cell would fan out from the center, but the easterly winds in the western sector would be considerably stronger than the westerly winds in the eastern sector, because of the momentum brought down from the easterly air current prevailing above, about 10,000 feet. This is the normal experience in squalls in this region at this season of the year.

Initially, the aircraft would experience a moderately enhanced headwind, which is suggested by the evidence of the Captain (updraft) and a passenger (air pocket). This would rapidly change to a strong tailwind, with possibly an element of downdraft, though it is improbable that any significant downdraft was experienced near the surface.

There would probably have been a pressure rise of the order of 2–3 millibars within the cell, which would have caused the altimeter of the aircraft to indicate a height 50–100 feet lower than the true height; that is, the aircraft would have actually been 50 to 100 feet higher than was registered on its altimeter. The relatively sudden change of wind from a moderate headwind to a strong tailwind experienced in the cell would cause a corresponding decrease in the airspeed of the aircraft.

OBSERVATIONS

1. The board has given close consideration to the question as to whether the Pilot-in-Command was justified in commencing the flight in the weather conditions that existed at the time of the take-off. That he had taken care to ascertain the nature of the approaching storm is clear from the questions that he posed to the meteorological forecaster. He was mainly concerned as to whether the thunderstorm approaching from the northeast was associated with a line squall and how fast and in

what direction it was moving. The forecaster rightly assured him that the thunderstorm had no association with any line squall and that it was a slow-moving local thunderstorm. The Pilot-in-Command also constantly watched the movement of the storm very closely and formed the opinion, which he expressed to the navigating officer, that he estimated it would pass about eight to ten miles north of the airport and, therefore, after taking off, he was prepared to fly off the track to the west, in order to avoid the storm. The moderate rain that fell at the time of the take-off did not cause him any concern, as the conditions were considerably above BOAC's minimum, and as he had taken off in as bad conditions on several previous occasions, he did not at any time consider the need to abandon the take-off.

Neither he nor the forecaster could have been aware that the thunderstorm cell was forming close to the west of the airport along the take-off path from Runway 25, since the associated cloud development was obscured by a lower cloud. Kano airport was equipped with storm warning radar, capable of identifying storms some distance away but incapable of detecting the formation of a thunderstorm cell at close range.

The Board is not aware of any official notification to pilots prohibiting them from or advising them against take-off in, or in the vicinity of, thunderstorms.

The Board, therefore, is of the opinion that the Pilot-in-Command was justified in taking off in the prevailing conditions.

2. The effect of the weather conditions on the aircraft's performance when it was at the height of approximately 250 feet after taking off, has been closely investigated. It is clear from the meteorological analysis that a thunderstorm cell was developing in the area into which the aircraft was climbing. In the early stages of the climb the aircraft encountered an increased westerly wind component as it passed over the end of the runway. But when it reached approximately 250 feet, it became affected by a sudden reversal of wind direction of considerable magnitude, accompanied by heavy rain and possibly a downdraft. The effect of these conditions was to cause the aircraft to lose speed relative to the surrounding air and to lose height rapidly. The situation was aggravated by the fact that

the speed of the aircraft had become very close to its stalling speed. Throughout this period all engines were operating at a high degree of power but had no noticeable effect in preventing the rapid loss of height. The approximate path of the aircraft in elevation has been plotted from the take-off point to a point about 150 yards short of the first point of impact, and shows that the descent occurred in a very short period of time probably within the range of 5 to 15 seconds. It has not been possible to estimate the exact height and point at which the aircraft became affected by the cell conditions and, therefore, the rate of descent is largely a matter for conjecture. The rapid descent was in no way caused by the attitude of the aircraft which remained level throughout.

The Board of Enquiry dealt at some length with the question as to whether the accident might have been averted if the master control lever to increase the rpm's of all engines at the same time had been working, and concluded that it was doubtful it would have had any effect.

The opinion of the board was unanimous: The accident was the result of loss of height and air speed caused by the aircraft encountering, at approximately 250 feet, an unpredictable thunderstorm cell which gave rise to a sudden reversal of wind direction, heavy rain, and possible downdraft conditions.

The board then recommended two things:

(1) The International Civil Aviation Organization should be asked to consider setting up a technical committee to investigate the danger to aircraft taking off or landing when in close proximity to thunderstorms, and to frame recommendations to member states for the safer operation of aircraft in such conditions.

(2) As an interim measure, all pilots should be warned of the danger of taking off or landing when thunderstorms are in the vicinity.

The findings, conclusion, and recommendations were signed by the Board of Enquiry on July 18, 1956 and were published by Her Majesty's Stationery Office and widely distributed to the air transport industry and personnel. The full report could be purchased at three outlets in London, one in Edinburgh, Cardiff, Manchester, Bristol, Birmingham, and Belfast, or at any bookseller's in the United Kingdom.

Perhaps such widespread distribution accomplished some good. It may have reminded pilots what weathermen had been warning for years: Don't fly under the overhang of a thunderstorm.

There have been probably only one or two cases on record of any humor emanating from landings or take-offs in rain and turbulent conditions because there is nothing humorous about airplane crashes. Yet one incident on record, which happened at Miami, a city that has had its share of thunderstorm tragedies, is worth recording because it had a silly ending and no one was hurt except the aircraft.

On Friday, November 12, 1954, a National Airlines Lockheed *Lodestar* crashed while landing at Miami's International Airport. None of the eleven passengers or three crew members was injured, but they sure got wet.

The flight, known as Number 38, was ending a scheduled nonstop run from Meacham Airport at Key West on the last return of a daily operation of three round trips operated by National between these cities. The flight crew consisted of Captain Sherrel P. Whittaker, thirty-nine, Co-pilot Richard E. Alderson, thirty-three, and stewardess Elizabeth Gregory.

Because of the beastly weather which covered southern Florida this day, Flight 38 left Key West at two minutes after eight at night, some fifty-seven minutes behind schedule. It was loaded to a gross take-off weight of 18,128 pounds, 1,372 pounds under the maximum allowable. The *Lodestar,* a twin-engined, twin-tailed 14-passenger aircraft which had a distinguished record of passenger service in the U. S. and Canada, climbed easily from the Key West runway to its cruising altitude of 4,000 feet. The flight time to Miami was estimated at just forty-five minutes via the Homestead radio range, which is a holding point twenty-two miles southeast of Miami. Because of the bad weather, the alternate airport for the flight was designated as West Palm Beach, sixty-one miles north of Miami.

The flight droned northward through intermittent rain

clouds and was on instruments most of the time. The turbulence was severe and the pilot was forced to reduce the air speed to provide a meager measure of comfort to the bouncing passengers. At 8:12 P.M., the flight reported to Miami that it was estimating its arrival over the Homestead radio range at 8:45 P.M.

At 8:22, 8:29, and 8:33, the flight acknowledged special weather observations being radioed to it by the National Airlines radio dispatchers. All these indicated short periods of heavy rain, visibility under one mile, and a precipitation ceiling between 600 and 1,100 feet.

At 8:50 P.M., five minutes behind schedule because of the turbulence, the flight reported it was "over Homestead" and was immediately cleared by the Miami Approach Control to hold its position. The *Lodestar* circled in the storm for five minutes before it was cleared to fly to the Miami range station, located slightly more than five-and-a-half miles west of the instrument runway known as 9 Right. The flight was cleared to descend to 3,500 feet and then to 2,500 feet while approaching this range.

At 9:03 P.M., Flight 38 reported over the Miami range station and was cleared to come down to 1,500 feet and to proceed inbound for an instrument landing approach. The latest weather information was provided the flight at this moment, ". . . winds east-northeast, fifteen to twenty miles an hour, visibility one half mile." This was repeated.

The approach controller in the Miami Tower stared out through the glass windows to the west, straining in the dark to see the incoming flight. He waited for what he considered the normal time for the approach to be completed and then called the flight to ascertain where it was.

He received no reply to his repeated calls. He thought he saw lights at the end of the runway but they were not moving. He sent out the emergency alarm, and ambulances and fire reels raced to the end of the runway.

Flight 38 had been swallowed up in the rain.

And swallowed up is the only word for it.

The storm conditions hadn't seemed too bad to Capt. Whittaker as he made his approach to the Miami airport. He was using his Instrument Landing Approach system, but he was also able to maintain visible reference to the airport ahead of him. Passengers could see clearly the lights of Coral Gables and the city of Miami beyond. What they couldn't see was a cloud above them that towered over 30,000 feet and was settling with updrafts, downdrafts, and torrential rain, occasionally laced with lightning.

The Instrument Landing Approach system, which is used by all commercial and military airliners, is a system in which needles are lined up on the face of a circular dial to show the plane's reference to the runway on which it is intending to land. A vertical needle shows the plane's position in relation to the center of the runway. If the needle is too far to the right of the vertical line, the plane can be steered by the rudder slightly to the left until the needle is centered over the vertical line. And if the needle should stray to the left, it means the aircraft has veered to the left and must be corrected toward the right.

The horizontal needle shows the position of the aircraft in relation to its downward approach to the end of the runway. If the needle is too low on the glide path reference on the dial the plane is too low, and conversely, if the needle is too high the plane is too high. Lining up the needles vertically and horizontally will bring the aircraft to the end of the runway, and if the cloud ceiling is 200 feet or more and visibility is at least half a mile, the pilot goes on to land the aircraft.

Capt. Whittaker was flying on his instrument system, but he was also able to raise his eyes from time to time for split seconds to see that he was coming down in a correct manner and was heading for the center of the runway lights ahead.

When his *Lodestar* reached the outer marker, a radio reference point 4.4 miles due west of the runway, Capt. Whittaker looked up again and could clearly see the Miami runway lights in the distance. He switched on his landing lights and

This scene is familiar to anyone who has watched a summer thunderstorm charge across the land. It is unbelievable that some pilots would fly their planes into such threatening clouds. But they have. And a few have lived to boast about it. Most veteran commercial pilots give such storms a wide berth. (Photo by James Yarnell) lowered the flaps to 60 degrees to give the plane added lift and to slow it down slightly. The air speed dropped to 105 miles an hour, which was right on the button. The wheels were down and a check showed they were locked in position for the landing.

Rain speckled the windshield and the plane began to bounce slightly from turbulence.

Capt. Whittaker was moving close to the runway and he "flared out" his aircraft for the touchdown by moving back the trim mechanism to give a nose-up attitude so that the wheels could make a proper touch on the runway.

At this precise second of the final approach, all hell broke loose. The flight ran into an unexpected, intense tropical downpour. Visibility was cut to zero and a strong updraft was encountered. The captain felt the aircraft lifting and he lowered the nose to counteract the lift in order to stay as close to the runway as possible. At this moment, the closest runway lights were diffused in the water that covered the windshields and it was impossible for the crew to tell how far the aircraft was above the runway.

The updraft ceased, as could be expected. The aircraft suddenly dropped lower, as also could be expected. Capt. Whittaker pulled back on the control column to arrest the descent and poured on the power to the two engines. The aircraft did not respond. It crashed into the concrete runway, its propellers sending up showers of sparks which reflected in the river of water over the runway like fireworks by a lake.

The eleven passengers and the three crew members, unscathed, scrambled out of the narrow doorway of the *Lodestar* in less than one minute flat and jumped down into deep pools of water while blinded by the torrential downpour. One young woman who leaped from the doorway some four feet to the ground, as if the plane was going to explode at any second, hit the concrete in a legs-out position with a tremendous splash of cold water. As one of the other passengers gallantly struggled in the wind and rain to get her out of the pool, she shouted: "That's the last time I ever fly without my pants on!"

"Flight 810 Has Gone Off Our Scope" 6

ONE OF THE hidden dangers of thunderstorms is the sinister peril of hail and ice.

The thin-winged aircraft of the jet age are particularly susceptible to the problems of hail and icing because they enter danger areas at such great speed. Thus they may be in serious trouble before their pilots can take evasive action.

Hail and icing show no preference for any one of the many types of commercial airliners, but there are those pilots who believe it much safer to fly a piston-engine aircraft into hail and ice than the high-speed turboprop airliners or the modern jets. They may be right up to a point. The piston-type airliners have rubber boots inserted along the leading edges of the wings and along the leading edges of the tail. These boots are not found on turbo-airliners because they are bulky and contribute to the drag on the aircraft. There is an axiom among many jet and turboprop airliner pilots that the great speed of their modern machines will carry them through hail and icing so quickly that the problem is one of a few seconds' duration only. This, of course, is a fallacy that may some day cause them grave trouble, because speed increases the danger of both hail and icing.

Let's have a brief look at the conditions that produce these hazards in the atmosphere.

This is what happens to a modern jet when it penetrates a thunder-storm and encounters hail showers. This photograph of a RCAF T-33 shows the battering it took on the intake cowls and the nose. (Royal Canadian Air Force photo)

Hail is most often associated with the mature stage of thunderstorms. It is produced by the violent updrafts within the cells and is usually found at altitudes between 10,000 and 15,000 feet. There are often occasions when the thunderstorm cells are tilted, as we have seen, and this situation gives rise to a phenomenon that often traps pilots.

Hail can fall from clear skies. This may seem strange indeed, but the tilted cell is the cause. The hail is formed by the tremendous updrafts in the upper part of the slanted cells, and the weight of each ice stone carries it straight down. This means that hail can often be found beneath the protruding angle of the anvil. As one Air Force instructor frequently said to his trainees: "Never fly near a thunderstorm . . . there are too damn many variables . . . and never fly into one, either."

Icing conditions, which are much more common than hail and therefore are much more dangerous to aircraft, also occur in the upper regions of mature cells. Generally, icing conditions occur at the precise moment the cell has reached maturity.

Ice particles are created by the speed of the mighty updrafts. Water droplets are carried aloft so swiftly that they enter a strange world of supercooling. The droplets can actually be surrounded by temperatures as low as 55 degrees below zero and still remain as water until they strike a solid object. Then they freeze instantly.

When a supercooled water droplet impacts against the wing or the fuselage of an airliner, it freezes into an infinitesimal lump. The next one builds atop the first one, and so on and on, each droplet sticking like glue to the one beneath it and thus forming a solid ice foundation.

There is no satisfactory solution to the problem of icing. Deicing boots and heated propellers on conventional aircraft cannot solve the problem. Avoidance is the best possible solution, yet there are occasions when this is not always possible, particularly when an airplane is assigned to a crowded air corridor and cannot escape the troubles in its particular pathway.

High-speed aircraft are affected mostly during climbing periods and during letdowns toward their airports. Descending through icing areas can be reasonably safe, but only so long as a safe margin of air speed is maintained during final approach and landing. A missed approach is particularly serious under icing conditions because a heavy build-up of ice on the wings is most critical when rapidly increased power is essential after the missed approach.

The main effect of icing on an aircraft, however, is the changing of the aerodynamic properties of the wings by disturbing the flow of air over their surfaces. Lift is decreased, while drag is increased. This effect increases the stalling speed of the plane and lowers the air speed. Icing on the wings of an airplane becomes most serious when uneven formations spread rearward from the leading edge of the wings and cause ripples on the otherwise smooth surfaces. Under these circumstances there is an increased tendency for an aircraft to go into a spin because the controls are sluggish and unresponsive.

Icing creates a great many problems, most of them unsolved. For example, great chunks of accumulated ice will break off from the wings and from the propellers and slam against the fuselage of the airplane at high speed. The noise inside the plane is appalling, but serious damage to the aircraft is rare. However, when chunks of ice break away and lodge in the hinges of the ailerons and flaps, interfering with the proper controlling of the aircraft, the situation is serious. The increase in weight due to the building up of the accumulation is not always dangerous, unless the aircraft experiences an engine failure. That, in certain circumstances, such an accumulation can be critical, however, will soon be demonstrated.

Ice forming on the blades of the whirling propellers results in a reduction of thrust. Couple this with the loss of aerodynamic efficiency, and the pilot of the airliner can find himself in a difficult spot. His only alternatives are to descend into a temperature zone that will melt the ice accumulation or to climb above the icing and bear the increased weight for the remainder of the flight.

Sometimes chunks of ice on the propeller blades are not sloughed off until they reach a formidable size. This creates

Airframe manufacturers, aware of the problem of icing, subject fuselages and control surfaces to severe icing conditions in subzero cold chambers such as the one shown here at Weybridge, England, where Valiants and Vanguards are made. (Vickers-Armstrong photo)

dangerous propeller imbalance and can lead to extremely high vibration in the engine and force a shutdown of the affected power plant, usually at the very time when all the power is needed.

When ice forms on windshields it restricts the vision of the flight crew. It also clings to radio antennas, causing them to vibrate and snap off.

Ice can interfere with radio reception and often curtails radar scanning at the very time that radar is most important— the time when the aircraft is approaching a thunderstorm cell.

Ice plugs the pitot tubes (these are tubes protruding from the wings to measure the air speed of the plane). The altimeter and other important instruments can be affected by ice accumulation. Static vents in some airplanes are located in such a position that ice building up around them can disturb the airflow and cause further incorrect readings of the instruments which are essential to safe operation of the aircraft.

In a split second, ice can coat the carburetor and the air intake system of piston engine planes, reducing power, and in some cases causing complete engine failure. Pilots of piston engine airplanes should remember that icing is ever present in the carburetor system, caused by the rapid evaporation of fuel and the reduction in pressure. This can occur at any time when moisture is high and air temperature is above freezing.

Jet engines and turboprop power plants are actually gas turbine engines, and ice can form on the air intake cowlings as well as on the impeller and compressor blades near the front of these engines. Chunks of ice breaking off and slamming rearward can cause serious damage, while the accumulations of ice on the compressor blades can cause the loss of aerodynamic efficiency, set up vibration, and put out the fires that keep the fuel burning. Engine failure in a jet can be caused in a matter of seconds during severe icing conditions, the kind of conditions which occur at high altitudes in the upper part of thunderstorm cells.

As we have seen, when water droplets enter a supercooled area and strike an aircraft, each droplet freezes immediately.

Made-to-order icing clouds are provided by this specially built spray system in the Icing Research Tunnel of the Lewis Flight Propulsion Laboratory. Flight icing detectors and such full-scale aircraft components as wings, engine inlets, radomes, and windshields are studied under simulated flight icing conditions. (NACA photo)

Then the droplet releases its heat so that its internal temperature rises until zero centigrade is reached. At this temperature, the freezing caused by the impact of the aircraft on the droplet ceases, with the result that the rest of the droplet that has not yet had time to freeze begins to freeze more slowly because of cold surroundings and the evaporation which is taking place.

The infinitesimal fraction of the supercooled droplet that freezes on impact depends on the air temperature. When the mercury is very low, a large part of the droplet must freeze to supply enough heat to reach zero centigrade. When the temperature is higher, only a small part of the droplet freezes on impact, leaving a much greater amount to freeze more slowly.

After the impact, the speed of freezing of the rest of the droplet depends on the temperature of the metal skin of the aircraft. The higher the temperature of the skin, the slower the droplet will freeze and, as a consequence, the more it will spread from the point of impact before the freezing is completed. If the droplets pile on one another before the freezing of each is completed, the unfrozen droplets will mingle together and spread out, forming a solid sheet of ice. Therefore, the size of the droplets and the frequency with which they strike the aircraft skin decide the degree of formation of ice.

The amount of water collected by the aircraft over a given period of time is known to pilots as the "rate of catch." It varies with the water content in the clouds at the flight level, the size of the drops, the speed of the aircraft, and the type of wing. If the temperature is just right for icing conditions, the rate at which the ice will build up increases as the airplane's rate of catch increases.

At a given aircraft speed, small droplets tend to follow the airflow around the plane and are carried around the aircraft. However, the heavier droplets, because of their weight and size, tend to cross the airflow and strike the wings. Since these large supercooled drops cannot withstand the phenomenon of supercooling to the same degree as the smaller ones, they are most likely to be found in the lower levels of cold clouds. Also, since they require strong vertical updrafts to support them,

*A special camera is mounted beneath this AT-11 aircraft to photo-
graph water droplets at various stages in cumulo-nimbus clouds.
This research is being carried on by the Lewis Flight Propulsion
Laboratory of the National Advisory Committee for Aeronautics at
Cleveland, Ohio. Some droplets have been found to be cubes, not
round drops, as one would imagine.* (NACA photo)

they are most common in the clouds that have formed in unstable air, such as cumulo-nimbus thunderstorms.

As the air speed of an airplane increases, so does the number of water droplets struck. The radius of the curvature of the leading edge of the wings also has a direct bearing on the rate of catch. Thin jet wings catch more droplets per square inch of leading edge than do big thick wings.

This means that high-speed, thin-winged aircraft have the greatest rate of catch and must expect the most serious icing when the aircraft's skin temperature is at or below freezing and the aircraft flies through a cloud where there is a great deal of liquid in large droplet form.

Severe icing is a natural ingredient of turbulent cumulo-nimbus clouds, and occurs in the upper half of cells that are nearing the mature thunderstorm stage. Although it's a fact that there is a low water content in clouds whose temperatures are below minus 25 degrees centigrade, thunderstorms are an exception because their vertical currents carry droplets into colder regions.

It is reasonable to assume that many airplane disasters in thunderstorms have probably occurred very high in clouds between 14,000 and 20,000 feet, where icing conditions are most severe. There is on record an example of what happens in a thunderstorm when ice gathers alarmingly on an aircraft.

This tragedy occurred over the Rocky Mountains in 1956 and is a textbook picture of what a thunderstorm and icing can do to a modern airliner, even at very great heights.

At 5:30 P.M. on the blustery afternoon of December 9, 1956, a group of impatient air travelers standing in the crowded waiting room of Vancouver's International Airport heard, at long last, the announcement they had been waiting for: "Trans-Canada Air Lines Flight Eight-ten, *North Star* service for Calgary, Regina, Winnipeg, Toronto, and Montreal now loading at Gate Five . . . all aboard, please."

Fifty-eight men, women, and children squeezed through the swinging doors and hurried across the windy, rain-swept concrete to the gleaming silver aircraft ahead of them. At the plane's entrance, pretty Dorothy Bjornson, twenty-three, of Swan River, Manitoba, greeted each passenger with a cheerful smile. She was alone because this was a tourist flight, and she parried the bitter comments of the grumbling passengers with words of encouragement: "We'll soon be on our way . . . the weather's been holding us up." And indeed it had.

The airliner which they were now boarding had arrived in Vancouver during the early afternoon more than four hours behind schedule because of storms over the mountains and terrific head winds boosted aloft by the westerly gales so familiar to the Northwest at that time of year. In fact, the westbound flight had been so turbulent that Trans-Canada Air Lines had, at first, not intended to operate the return flight that day.

The weather over the entire West Coast from Alaska to Oregon was stormy and miserable. Dreary rain and howling winds —mixed with low swirling clouds and fog in the coastal regions, and snow blizzards with freezing rain, gale winds, and thunderstorms in the mountains—blanketed the land and water from the outer islands along the Pacific to the plains regions of Montana and Alberta.

When the TCA airliner had finally arrived at Vancouver with a full load of badly frightened passengers, it required a complete ground inspection and engine exhaust tests before being cleared for its next operation. The mechanical check-out was finally completed at 3:45 P.M. Pacific standard time.

The general weather in Vancouver continued to worsen, as it often does in the afternoon at that time of year, but TCA decided the return flight could operate because Edmonton, Alberta, was clear and so were all the other cities to the east. Calgary alone was doubtful, being held down by rain and fog. Having made the decision to operate the flight, TCA notified Capt. Allan Clarke and First Officer John Boon, and the two pilots sped from their Vancouver homes to the airport to plan their flight. They arrived at 4:45 P.M. and went directly to the weather briefing office.

The two fliers spent some time with the airways weather forecaster, studying the weather charts over the mountains, particularly the vast, inhospitable region lying northward of the U. S.-Canada border—the first hundred miles of the flight plan.

After briefing, both pilots went to the operations room and chatted for several minutes with pilots who had just crossed westward over the mountains. As a result of these consultations, they decided to operate routinely to Calgary, 400 miles over the Rockies. They would have more than enough fuel to fly north to Edmonton or eastward to Regina, Saskatchewan, if Calgary weather failed to clear up. But there was every indication that the fog would lift in the cool of the evening. Both Clarke and Boon signed their flight plan at 5:14 P.M. This was the signal for the TCA flight dispatcher to load 11,400 pounds of high-octane gasoline into the giant wings of the aircraft, which brought the take-off weight to 76,850 pounds. Clarke and Boon then ran through the rain and capricious gusts of wind to their airliner.

Meanwhile, back in the crowded waiting room, passengers for several TCA flights milled around the ticket counters waiting for long-delayed announcements. Four of the impatient travelers were top players on the Saskatchewan Rough Riders football team returning home after the annual Shrine all-star football game at Vancouver the day before. Two were U. S. imports, Mario De Marco, twenty-eight, of Boonton, New Jersey, who had played with the Detroit Lions, and famous center Mel Becket, an Indiana University graduate. The other two players were Ray Syrnyk, of Redwater, Alberta, and Gordon Sturtridge, of Winnipeg. Shrine officials had insured each of the players for $40,000, in addition to the insurance they may have bought for themselves.

In fact, the long delay in the flight and the bad weather had made the terminal's flight insurance machine busier than usual. Passengers for Flight 810 bought a total of $2,000,000 in policies.

Behind the football players, who were laughing and arguing with several newspaper sports writers, stood a group of six Chinese passengers. One of them was Kwang Song, whose address was The Bowery, in New York City. He was returning from a flight to Hong Kong and had left the Crown Colony under the watchful eye of British Intelligence. His progress through Canada was under the surveillance of the Royal Canadian Mounted Police and the Federal Bureau of Investigation. Kwang was carrying $80,000 in U. S. currency in his money belt and it was believed that he was bringing it to New York City, to a travel agency, to pay the fares of Chinese students who had been studying in U. S. universities and whom the Red Chinese government hoped to persuade to return to Red China to help the Peoples Republic's technological program, particularly in nuclear projects.

The announcement of Flight 810 ended the clicking of the insurance machine and clusters of people began to elbow their way to the gate. Mrs. Walter Rowan, wife of the Calgary TCA office manager, gave a great sigh of relief. The long wait had made her children, Susan and Patrick, restless and bored. Their father had tried to calm them several times, but finally had given up. Another passenger was Mrs. Eleanor Welch, who had been visiting her mother in Vancouver and was anxious to return to Toronto and her two daughters. One of them, Judy, was Miss Toronto of that year.

In less than five minutes, all the passengers save one were aboard the aircraft. Racing into the terminal from a screeching cab came Calvin Jones, famous 1955 All-American guard from Iowa, who had played for the West in the previous day's Shrine game. He had missed an earlier flight and TCA agents "squeezed" him into Flight 810. He took one of the two seats in the very rear of the passenger compartment normally reserved for the stewardesses. It was the last empty seat left in the plane and was free because Miss Bjornson was the only stewardess aboard.

On the flight deck of the *North Star* airliner, Capt. Clarke agreed with the TCA flight dispatcher to load an additional 800 pounds of fuel into the wings. This would bring the total weight of gasoline to 13,394 pounds, as the wings had contained some gasoline before the loading commenced. While this was being done, Clarke and Boon worked on their cockpit check-out.

With the additional fuel loaded and the cockpit check-out completed, Clarke brought the four Merlin engines to higher life and eased the lumbering aircraft through the drizzle to the north end of the Vancouver airport. Then he ran up the engines, double-checking every phase—cylinder head heat, magnetos, radiator flap positions, glycol temperature, oil, fuel metering instruments, and so on. His fellow pilots knew all too well that Clarke's run-ups could be exhaustive and damned irritating. He was known the length and breadth of the TCA system as "Granny" Clarke. The nickname stemmed from his meticulousness and from the fact that he was never known to have accepted an unnecessary risk, even when serving with distinction in the RAF Bomber Command in the Middle East during World War II.

The run-up completed, Clarke swung the giant aircraft to the take-off position on Runway 11. Simultaneously, co-pilot Boon requested take-off clearance and final routing.

The tower voice rasped: "Okay Flight Eight-one-zero . . . cleared for take-off on Runway Eleven . . . winds east-southeast at 20 knots, gusting to 30 . . . altimeter zero nine . . ."

Clarke moved the four throttles to full forward, and the Merlins roared to full life, drowning out all other sounds inside as well as outside the silver airliner. The plane moved slowly at first and then, as it gathered speed in the gusty wind, lifted off easily at 110 knots after traveling over 4,700 feet of runway.

"Vancouver Tower . . . ah, this is Eight-one-zero . . . off at 6:10 . . ." radioed Boon as the aircraft disappeared into the swirling mists, its blinking red belly and taillights visible for several more seconds to the tower.

Clarke banked the heavy aircraft into a tight right turn and headed southward toward a radio intersection point on his route, known as West Ham, located eight miles away on the muddy tidelands of the Straits of Georgia. He held the plane on the exact flight plan, keeping to the assigned 3,000 feet until he reached West Ham. Then he banked left and eastward, climbing steadily at 500 feet per minute through occasional rain showers.

According to the Air Traffic Control flight plan which had been issued to him prior to take-off, Clarke shuttled along the south leg of the Vancouver Low Frequency radio range, hoping to reach an altitude of 10,000 feet by the next radio reporting point, aptly named Mud Bay. Pilots flying from Vancouver eastward over the Coastal Range of the Rockies like to get as much altitude as they can by the time they reach the first line of peaks. This reassures them, even in fine weather.

The 10,000-foot altitude was reached at 6:28 P.M.

Boon reported Flight 810 "by Mud Bay" at 6:29 P.M. The flight continued uneventfully eastward and upward on a pathway in the sky approximately ten miles north of the U. S.-Canadian border. The plane was climbing through light clouds, and in the passenger compartments, front and rear, the signs remained glowing: FASTEN YOUR SEAT BELTS—BOUCLEZ VOS CEINTURES. Heavier cloud formations lay ahead, and occasionally vast cumulus castles would appear as brilliant flashes of lightning played over the mountains with awesome explosions of orange and brilliant blue puffballs of electric fire.

The Vancouver Air Traffic Center now cleared Flight 810 to Calgary, to cross over and report by the town of Abbotsford in the foothills, Cultus Lake, and thence over the Coastal Range toward Calgary.

Six minutes later, still climbing at 500 feet per minute and making excellent time, the flight reported: "Leaving 13,000 feet over Abbotsford."

Still later: "By Cultus Lake at 6:40" radioed Boon, as the *North Star* climbed through 15,000 feet, a mile above the menacing mountain tops below.

It is evident from the radio communications, preserved to this day on tape, that the flight was making excellent time, climbing at an estimated ground speed of 240 miles an hour with the help of a powerful tail wind. At this precise moment the aircraft was sixty miles east of Vancouver and approximately one mile north of the border which divides the state of Washington from the province of British Columbia. So far, the flight had been reasonably smooth. None of the radio communications had mentioned anything to the contrary.

But ahead lay trouble.

The first indication that the plane was running into a mountain of thunderstorms occurred when it reported passing through 16,000 feet. Boon radioed they were encountering light to moderate turbulence and that ice had started to coat the surface of the wings.

Flight 810 was now in the grip of the peculiar weather conditions that develop over the coastal ranges of the Rocky Mountains, conditions that have claimed many aircraft over the past few years. These peculiar weather conditions are called "mountain waves."

When air crosses a range of mountains, a series of waves, spaced at intervals of two to twenty miles, are usually set in motion. Each wave marks the place where the air leaps vertically to form a crest. The strongest wave in each system is the one closest to the mountain range.

Have you ever watched a river where it strikes a rock? The waves and ripples form downstream from the rock. Mountain waves are formed in much the same way, and, because of prevailing westerly winds, are most common on the eastern side of the ranges. If the air is moist enough, clouds form in these undulating currents. These clouds are distinctive and easily recognizable by pilots in daytime. Strange shapes—known to weathermen and pilots, according to their appearance, as *cap clouds, rotor clouds,* and *lenticular clouds*—indicate that mountain waves are present.

Cap clouds look very much like caps crowning the tops of the mountain ranges and often stretch down the eastern slopes. The bases of cap clouds are usually below the peaks and their tops a few thousand feet above the peaks. These clouds bother commercial aircraft only because they conceal the peaks, some-

This high mountain-wave cloud, shown here over California, indicates high-level turbulence. Mountain waves can cause clouds up to 100,000 feet. They are particularly troublesome to jets. (U. S. Air Force photo)

times hiding strong downdrafts on the leeward sides. Yet they are a menace to small planes and have caused many an unwary pilot to fly to his death.

Rotor clouds, so called because they roll clockwise away from the mountains, form on the eastern slopes of mountain ranges in the Western United States and Canada. Rotor clouds may extend as high as 30,000 feet, and can actually cause the formation of thunderstorms. They often hide fierce currents and prodigious amounts of supercooled water droplets.

Lenticular clouds form at the crests of mountain waves. They are elongated and smooth, somewhat like almonds in shape. They often extend, layer upon layer, as high as 100,000 feet and stretch for hundreds of miles along the tops of mountain ranges. Lenticulars disclose that mountain waves exist.

Downdrafts in mountain waves quite often reach a speed of 2,000 feet per minute and they have been recorded as high as 5,000 feet per minute. They are so strong that an aircraft flying parallel to the range can be forced downward to the ground or may be carried into the side of the range. On the western side of a rotor cloud, there is an updraft which smart pilots can use to gain altitude. On the eastern side, a downdraft occurs which is a potential source of minor difficulty for large aircraft, and a severe hazard for light airplanes.

Turbulence is most severe in the regions atop rotor clouds, and is comparable to the turbulence found in thunderstorms. A glider designed to stand a stress of 10 G's broke up in a mid-air mountain wave during a recent California experiment. At very high altitudes of 40,000 feet and more, pilots have reported extreme turbulence even while flying over the smooth lenticular clouds. Yet turbulence may be found at any level.

Due to a phenomenon best known to physicists, an increase in the speed of the mountain waves can cause a decrease in pressure. There have been actual cases in which altimeters of planes flying through mountain waves have read 3,000 feet higher than they should have.

Shortly after 6:45 P.M. on this night of December 9, TCA's

A rotor cloud is peculiar to mountainous regions and alerts fliers to the presence of mountain waves. This remarkable sky display was photographed near Independence, California. Cloud formations of this type are common but not always so well developed as this one. (U. S. Weather Bureau photo)

Lenticular clouds such as these, which appear to be delicate sculptures in the sky, are a warning to pilots that mountain waves exist. (U. S. Weather Bureau photo)

Flight 810 was experiencing turbulence and icing conditions. Through the loud crackling of static caused by lightning discharges around him, Clarke was barely able to contact a westbound TCA flight twenty miles to the north. The plane was a *Super Constellation* and the pilot was Jack Wright, one of Clarke's good friends.

The two pilots chatted for a moment through the noise as Clarke pressed for more information about the weather conditions at the higher altitudes. He was still flying in icing conditions and was battling increasing turbulence. Capt. Wright was reassuring. He reported that the cloud tops were at 20,000 feet and the winds up there were at a good 90 miles an hour from the west. This meant that, if he climbed a little higher, Clarke would be out of the storm and could ride the high winds into Calgary. Capt. Wright further reported that his *Super Connie* was now picking up ice in its descent toward Vancouver, but he didn't think it sufficiently dangerous to deter his projected return trip eastbound later in the evening. He said he had every intention of flying his return trip at 20,000 feet and expected to be free of worry.

Another TCA aircraft over the mountains now reported to Flight 810.

It was a *Viscount,* bound from Vancouver to Edmonton, climbing at 1,000 feet per minute through the clouds thirty miles north of Clarke. Fully loaded and carrying Eastern newspapermen who had covered the Shrine game, and who were on the first-class *Viscount* flight because of their expense accounts, the aircraft reported clear skies at 21,000 feet, just above the cloud tops.

Clark and Boon gritted their teeth and elected to go higher.

At precisely 6:48 P.M., the flight was at 19,000 feet and Boon reported they were fighting "extreme turbulence." This would be the area in the thunderstorm where the cells were almost fully matured and the turbulence at its worst. The aircraft would be pitching, diving, climbing and yawing, pounding the passengers unmercifully.

But clear skies were just four minutes away, and the *North*

Using electronic tracking systems, as well as specially instrumented gliders such as the one shown here, research is being conducted to determine atmospheric conditions associated with airflow over mountain ranges. A turbulent rotor cloud is seen in the left foreground. (U. S. Air Force photo)

Star continued ever upward, searching for smooth air and stability. Clarke raised TCA operations in Vancouver, who in turn passed on his next request to Air Traffic Control. He sought permission to climb to 21,000 feet. This was immediately granted.

At this moment, the *North Star* would be in the vicinity of the Hope radio intersection, an invisible marker traveling north and south from the village of Hope located in the beautiful and rugged Fraser River valley astride the Trans-Canada Highway. Aircraft crossing this marker are required to report their position to Vancouver, but there is no evidence that Clarke and Boon so reported. This omission was probably due to the fact they had their hands full attempting to keep the pitching aircraft on an even keel. One can feel deeply sympathetic for the fifty-nine passengers and the lone Miss Bjornson. They were experiencing the terrors of a mountain thunderstorm with all the updrafts and downdrafts associated with such violence worsened by the rows of mountain ranges over which they were crossing. They would be blinded by lightning every second or two while knowing that two miles below them were the spires of mountaintops that stretched beneath the cloak of snow and clouds for hundreds of miles in every direction. The only emergency airport was the little one at the village of Hope, snuggled in a valley and cloaked in heavy fog.

Clarke and Boon were battling for their lives, fighting the ice that coated the wings, propellers, windshield, the rudder, tail and fuselage. Now they stared in utter disbelief at the red light which suddenly blazed brightly on the instrument panel, standing out like a beacon from the other subdued lights, including the measured flickering from the tiny green lights that indicated the electronic searching of the aircraft surfaces for ice accumulations.

The red light was the fire warning for the number-two engine, adjacent to the port side of the passenger compartment.

"Ah . . . it looks like we had a fire in number-two engine . . . shut down number two . . ." crackled the message to Vancouver.

Mountain ranges create their own weather, which is always a problem to fliers. This photograph was taken in 1963 during a flight over the Western Rockies beneath a typical mountain storm. It isn't often that peaks are so easily visible. (Photo by James Yarnell)

At this second, the tossing aircraft was somewhere over the Manning Provincial Forest, five miles north of the U. S.-Canadian border, 120 miles due east of Vancouver, and thirty-five miles southeast of the village of Hope.

The passengers could not have known of the red light in the cockpit and the tense radio messages that followed its discovery. But they might have noticed that the throbbing engine sounds had decreased noticeably. A spotlight undoubtedly played over the huge Merlin engine from which the warning had been received. The light probably revealed the propeller, coated in ice, standing stark and unmoving. The exhaust, ordinarily red, would have been cold and black.

Clarke now radioed Vancouver that he could see neither fire nor smoke but had shut down the engine as a precaution. This decision deprived the plane of one fourth of its power.

Was Clarke overly cautious, as his nickname "Granny" implied?

It is the first instinct of any pilot to reach for the feathering mechanism when the fire-warning light appears. Yet Clarke and Boon must have known that *North Stars* were notorious for flashing fire warnings when no fires existed in the engines. On one occasion, a TCA *North Star* en route from Toronto to Winnipeg had all four engine warnings flash at the same time. The aircraft was over the lakehead cities of Fort William and Port Arthur at a height of 19,000 feet. The pilot calmly radioed that all four warning lights had appeared but he could perceive no sign of any smoke and was proceeding normally to Winnipeg.

Clarke had elected to shut down one engine. Then he made another crucial decision. He decided to turn back to Vancouver, back through the violent thunderstorm cells and the mountain waves and the ice and the prospects of a head wind of probably 90 miles an hour. He would return through the treacherous updrafts and downdrafts of a storm becoming more violent by the minute, with an almost full load of fuel, a full passenger compartment, heavy freight and baggage, and one engine inoperative.

But Clarke was commander of the airplane and his was the

ultimate authority for its safety. He felt that it was safer to turn back rather than to continue on to Calgary. His radio rasped through the torment of the storm: "Ah . . . this is Eight-one-zero . . . request descent clearance to Vancouver vee-ah Cultus Lake and Abbotsford. . . . Over."

Clarke had the alternative of making a left turn to the north and flying thirty miles to the area from which the *Super Constellation* had just reported, then heading for Vancouver on an airway that would have permitted him to descend over the Fraser River valley away from the turbulence and the storm. This route might also have helped melt some of the ice on the wings.

Nevertheless, Clarke elected to return over the same route that he had followed outbound. He therefore made a turn to the right, headed south for a few seconds and then turned right again, facing west into the thunderstorms that had already cost him a great deal of trouble. He reported his change to the south and to the west and ended the static-clogged conversation with "holding at 19,000 feet." Further contacts from Flight 810 requested return via Green Airway Number One with immediate descent.

The time was 6:53 P.M.

From this moment on, the handling of Flight 810's messages was complicated, due in part to the fact that TCA's radio center at Vancouver was handling most of the calls from Clarke and Boon, and relaying them to Air Traffic Control. Static also delayed the urgent messages, and finally TCA permitted the flight to talk directly to Vancouver Control. This was accomplished by 6:56 P.M.

Through the static, it took the flight one full agonizing minute to explain to Air Traffic Control that the plane was losing altitude and the crew needed immediate clearance to get down.

At 6:57 P.M., Flight 810 was given clearance to "maintain 14,000 feet via Green Number One and report by Hope."

This was an instruction for Flight 810 to descend to 14,000 feet on an airway known as Green Number One and report as soon as it crossed over the Hope radio intersection.

Was someone confused?

Green Airway Number One was located twenty-five or thirty miles north of Flight 810 and Clarke had radioed clearly he was turning south not north.

Did Air Traffic Control think that Clarke was much further north than he really was?

Was the controller ordering him to Green Number One in accordance with his requests so that he could get down to a much lower altitude to help him under the storm?

Is it possible that the confusion of the static and the relaying of messages from the flight to TCA to Air Traffic Control caused a mix-up as to the exact location of the plane?

Is it possible that Clarke and Boon thought they already were in the vicinity of Green Airway One?

Hardly. They had reported their position all the way and had been on their rightful airway on an eastern heading of 64 degrees. For a clearer explanation of the confusing circumstances, it is necessary to describe Green Airway One.

According to the Victoria-Vancouver National Topographical map of the Canadian Department of Mines, Technical Survey, Aeronautical Edition, published in October 1955, Green Airway Number One is the westbound air corridor, twelve miles in width, crossing over the various ranges of the Rocky Mountains, with a heading toward the town of Princeton from the east of 245 degrees.

At Princeton the course deviates slightly, moving southwest on a heading of 238 degrees, and this heading continues right through to the Vancouver radio range. From the town of Princeton, snuggled deep in one of the many north and south valleys of the Rockies, to the next village west of it, the village of Hope, the minimum altitude shown is 9,100 feet.

From Hope westward, the minimum drops to 8,000 feet because of the broadening of the Fraser River valley. This altitude is to be strictly maintained until the aircraft crosses a radio fan marker, on a north-south line from Abbotsford, where the minimum falls sharply to 5,200 feet.

Pilots faced with an east-wind landing would often cross the Vancouver range at this height, travel over the waters of the Straits of Georgia and then bank eastward and drop lower and lower for the landing, safe in the knowledge that nothing was underneath them except water and muddy tidelands.

Green Airway Number One and its established minimums may be important in the light of the next succession of events.

Heavy static persisted. Weathermen refer to static in the vicinity of thunderstorms as precipitation static. Aircraft flying near an external electrical field may accumulate a strong charge, and the static resulting from the escape of this electrical charge into the surrounding air can seriously interfere with radio communication. Since precipitation static is likely to be most severe when radio reception is vital to the safe operation of the aircraft, pilots are urged to study carefully all the conditions that can cause such interference.

Sometimes static is the friction resulting from the passage of dry dust or sand particles along the metal skin of the airplane.

Ice crystals also have an effect similar to dust or sand. The appearance of hoarfrost on the windows of an aircraft is a warning that ice crystals are present. Snow crystals and freezing rain rarely cause precipitation static, nor does rain itself, except on rare occasions.

However, all clouds have electrical fields. The greater the turbulence in the cloud, the stronger the external field is likely to be, and the strongest external fields are closely associated with thunderstorms. When an aircraft flies through the anvil, ice crystals as well as the external electrical fields give considerable static and can cause serious disruption of radio communication.

Capt. Clarke and his co-pilot Boon fought their way steadily westward and, at one minute after seven o'clock, Air Traffic Control asked the flight for its estimated time to the Hope radio intersection. The flight replied through the storm: "Five minutes, roughly."

Air Traffic Control then asked if the flight was able to maintain 14,000 feet, and the answer from the plane was: "Yes."

The flight was then asked by the controller to make its revised flight plan read "14,000 feet or above at 7:03 P.M."

A few minutes after this brief cryptic exchange, the controller was concerned that the flight had not reported over the Hope intersection at the end of the five-minute interval, and at 7:07 P.M. he called the flight once again and asked if Hope had been reached.

"Negative," shouted Boon through the static.

This would indicate that Flight 810 was struggling against a terrific head wind, as reported earlier from the westbound *Super Constellation* by its commander, Jack Wright.

No wonder the Vancouver controller was concerned. And he was not the only one worried with the airliner's battle with the mountain storm. Radar operators of the North American Air Defense (Norad) located on the lonely Birch Bay peninsula, northwest of Bellingham, Washington, had noted Flight 810's eastward movements as a matter of routine, after the flight plan had been relayed to them by the Vancouver Tower. The flight was a matter for casual observance as part of the constant scanning of the busy skies over Seattle, Vancouver, Bellingham, Victoria, and Patricia Bay.

But when Flight 810 turned from its prescribed course and headed westward where no plane had been reported to the Norad Control Center, the tiny white blip became an "alert."

Birch Bay contacted the Vancouver Tower and learned that the little blip with the big storm clouds around it was the *North Star* returning with one engine out. As a result of this information, the tortuous course of the flight would now be watched with infinite care. The distance of the plane could be determined by the radarscope, but it was impossible to determine the height of the aircraft. Yet it could be clearly seen over the sawtooth peaks beneath it.

"By Hope at 7:10," radioed Flight 810, and the Vancouver controller breathed a sigh of relief. This message indicated that Flight 810 was making a ground speed of only 90 miles an hour, however, with the nose winds being well over 100 miles an hour.

But the struggling airliner was still in trouble. The increased roar of the static forced Clarke and Boon to use the eastbound *Viscount* (TCA's Flight Four, with the newsmen aboard) as a relay unit to forward their messages to Air Traffic Control. Clarke requested, by this relay, immediate permission to descend to 10,000 feet. It was quickly granted to him. This meant that Flight 810, still in the violent updrafts and downdrafts, was only 2,000 feet above the jagged peaks of the Coastal Range.

Air Traffic Control now radioed the flight and cleared it to the Vancouver Low Frequency Range "at 8,000 feet or above and remain at this frequency." This communication was acknowledged by the flight.

In the confusion of the ear-splitting static and the struggle to keep the aircraft from being sucked or shoved into the mountains did Clarke and Boon realize they were in an area where the minimums were 9,600 feet when they heard the clearance to 8,000 feet?

Did Vancouver Air Traffic Control believe the flight was on the Green Airway, when in reality it was some thirty miles south of the Airway and in a region where the jagged Rockies reached to 8,000 feet?

Even Clarke's request to descend to 10,000 feet left him with very little margin for downdrafts, especially when we remember that mountain thunderstorms had carried airliners downward at speeds as high as 5,000 feet per minute.

But the situation was desperate, and onward and downward plunged the ice-coated airliner.

Residents of Chilliwack, British Columbia, a small community on the Trans-Canada Highway some 20 miles northwest of this drama in the skies, later reported that at this time they heard tremendous thunderclaps from the mountain areas and rushed from their homes to stare in awe and fright at the fantastic displays of lightning and listen to the earsplitting reverberations of the thunder.

Up in those clouds, Flight 810 acknowledged the control

center's instruction clearing it to the Low Frequency Range at 8,000 feet or above.

Many pilots would have turned on the dead engine at this point, deciding that in an aircraft inexorably sinking to destruction, extra power was more important than the risk of the fire. Clarke elected to follow the book.

The Birch Bay radar operators were the only people to witness the next episode. It was a spine chilling sight—the blip which was Flight 810 suddenly disappeared from the radar screen. The radar sweep made three more trips over the scope while the operators stared in disbelief at the fading pattern. The blip did not reappear. Controllers claim it is a frightening sight to be watching the blip of an aircraft on their radar and see it disappear . . . it indicates a disaster usually. In an Air Traffic Control Center it spells near panic. Here, one of the operators phoned the Vancouver Tower and yelled: "Your Flight 810 has gone off our scope."

Indeed it had. Flight 810 was dead. It had exploded to smithereens 7,940 feet up on Mount Slesse, just thirty feet below the topmost granite spire.

The crash site was within three miles of the U. S.-Canada border, a clear indication that Clarke had followed his return flight path to the very letter. He had flown eastward on the recognized air corridor on a heading of 64 degrees and had returned according to the book, on a heading of 244 degrees. And the minimum safe altitude for this corridor in which he was descending was 9,600 feet.

The exact time his *North Star* airliner passed over the Hope radio intersection, which incidentally is over the very center of Chilliwack Lake, was known to Air Traffic Control. The path of the plane was known to the Norad radar controller. Yet, despite these known facts it took five months to find the wreckage. It was found by sheer luck only after an amateur mountain climber became lost in a snowstorm.

After the flight's blip went off the radar screen, the authorities took two and a half hours to decide the flight was "definitely missing." Not until 9:35 P.M. was it officially reported as overdue. The Royal Canadian Air Force (RCAF) ordered its CF-100 all-weather jet interceptors into the air as the first move of what was to become the largest air search in Canadian history. But the all-weather jet fighters ran into bad weather and were forced to limp back to their airfield.

Flying Officer H. S. Gamblin, a navigator on one of the jets, said the turbulence over the mountains was so severe that he was torn from his safety belt and knocked partially unconscious, while his pilot fought to control the pitching, yawing interceptor.

Another officer who took part in the first phase of the search that night recalled on his return to the air base: "We were thrown around so much that our safety straps were breaking and our equipment flew all over the place. I never saw such violence before."

The next morning, December 10, 1956, Canadian Army paratroopers flew to Vancouver ready to be dropped into the mountains if the wreckage was sighted, and the first group of eighteen planes took off to search the mountains. The search planes were confused by a report from a group of guests at a mountain lodge near the village of Hope. They said they had heard a tremendous explosion fifty minutes after the last report from the missing plane and that it had seemed to come from a southeasterly direction. Reports also poured into search headquarters of an explosion having been seen and heard in the Fraser River valley. But all these stories proved groundless. The violent explosions were just the normal drumming of the thunderstorms, with that special violence peculiar to mountain areas.

The Royal Canadian Air Force spent weeks flying over the mountains and through the treacherous passes, clear one minute and cloaked in swirling fog the next, one minute raining and the next minute snowing. Much of their time was spent in the vicinity of two mountains, one named Silvertip and the other Cheam. Through rifts in the cloud cover, observers shot hundreds of photos of these two mountains, the tops, the sides, and the pine-studded foothills. However, both these mountains

On the towering granite peaks of Mount Slesse rests a Trans-Canada Air Lines (now Air Canada) North Star airliner and a full complement of crew and passengers. The bodies and wreckage are still there. This photograph was taken by the author from a search helicopter.

were considerably east of the last reported position of the aircraft and why they were ever picked for such careful study is puzzling.

During one afternoon of the search, there were twenty-four official planes over the area as well as twenty-six civilian planes ill-equipped to fly over mountain regions. The Canadian government was forced to step in and ban all flying over the region except for official search planes. A number of enthusiastic amateur mountain climbers rushed into the wilderness. Later, many of them had to be rescued, some by helicopter.

But still no trace of Flight 810.

Had the RCAF paid a little more attention to two "eyewitness" reports from the vicinity of Chilliwack River and the Trans-Canada Highway, they might have been able to pinpoint the scene of the crash. For instance, a soldier parked off the highway with a girl friend was, for some unknown reason, looking south over the mountain range when he saw a vivid explosion in the sky. He didn't know of the plane crash but he reported the phenomenon to the RCMP at Hope. The RCMP in turn passed along the information to the RCAF. But the most significant clue of all came from a trapper who had been camping on the Chilliwack River. At the very time of the flight's disappearance, he had witnessed through the snowstorm a tremendous explosion of orange flame atop one of the peaks, about eight miles from him. He immediately made two compass fixes to determine the location. Then he reported the unexplained occurrence to the RCMP at Chilliwack. This information also was turned over to the search authorities.

If a line had been drawn straight south from the soldier's parking place it would have intersected the two converging lines of the trapper's fix over a mountain known as Mt. Slesse. This 8,000-foot peak was close enough to a fine road and a lumber camp for the search parties to have investigated it on foot as well as by plane and helicopter. But this was not done, and finally the search petered out. Flight 810 was listed among the missing, as so many other aircraft had been in the past over the treacherous Rockies.

It was not until five months later—Sunday, May 12, 1957—
that a trio of mountain climbers became lost and turned up the
first clue to the location of the lost plane. The climbers were
Elfreda Pigou, a blonde amateur alpinist, and her two compan-
ions, Geoffrey Walker and David Cathcart, all from Vancouver
and on a week-end excursion into the snow-covered peaks.

On the night before—Saturday, May 11—the three had made
camp on the 1,900-foot level of the east face of Mt. Slesse and
at 7 A.M., they started up the dangerous slopes. Six hours later,
at the 7,500-foot level, a raging blizzard overtook them and
they became lost in the swirling snow of the howling gale.
While they huddled together, a piece of paper whipped around
and then fluttered into the tiny circle they made. Elfreda
grabbed at it. A piece of paper near a mountaintop was indeed
an unusual discovery.

The three studied it as the snow stung their eyes and the
winds threatened to topple them down the steep slope. The
scrap of paper was part of a map of the airways approach to the
airport at Sydney, Nova Scotia.

What was a map of the Sydney airport doing on Mt. Slesse,
obviously unfaded by the sun and snow? The trio discussed
their find for some time and when the blizzard stopped, as
abruptly as it began, they spread out and began to search the
deep snow that clung dramatically to the granite slope. A glint
in the sunlight caught their attention and they made their way
carefully along their ropes, digging in with their ice axes as
they inched toward the mirror-like object. It turned out to be a
slab of aluminum sheeting and on it the following letters and
numerals were inscribed: CA 37-3-2000-63B.

They looked around for further clues. Finding none, they
made their way down the slopes in the late afternoon to land
back in Vancouver that night. On Monday morning, May 13,
the three took the aluminum sheet and the torn map to the
Mounties, who, in turn, rushed the finds to the Trans-Canada
Air Lines regional operations center. It took a while to check
the serial number. Then the electrifying news came back from
Montreal. The piece of metal was from the wing of the missing

airliner, and the map was part of the regulation equipment of a TCA pilot.

Police and airline officials moved fast. They brought in skilled mountain climbers and a fleet of helicopters. They first established a camp on Mt. Slesse's east face at 2,500 feet and followed this up by the establishment of a second camp at 5,000 feet. The weather was unusually clear with occasional cloudy intervals.

After two days of probing the treacherous upper slopes below the awesome granite peaks of Slesse, an expert alpinist named Walter Broad found some grim evidence: a twelve-foot section of fuselage, a child's shoe, a handkerchief, a tiny hand, six-inch bits of luggage material, a pair of men's pajamas. All bore evidence of violence, but none was marked by the blackening of fire.

Climbing upward an inch at a time, the mountaineers found evidence that the airliner had collided with the peak of Slesse only thirty feet from the top. Shattered and blackened granite marked the spot where Flight 810 had blown to smithereens. Fragments of rock fell away when touched. Imbedded at the spot were wires of the pilot's headphones. The outline of his head and cap was clearly visible. Trailing from this point down the steep sides of the rock were the plane's steel control cables. About 100 feet below was a twisted propeller and a piece of fuselage twisted into unrecognizable junk.

Half a mile below this, at the foot of a sheer drop, were twin hummocks of snow, and here the principal wreckage and the bodies lay buried.

Meanwhile the attorney-general's department of the province of British Columbia had been working around the clock gathering from Trans-Canada Air Lines all sorts of identification material which had been collected since the flight disappeared. This had been painstakingly gathered by TCA from all over Canada, the United States, and the Orient.

All was ready now to retrieve the bodies, identify them, conduct autopsies, and send them home for burial.

Coroner Glen McDonald of Vancouver was assigned to conduct an inquest into the tragedy, as is necessary under provincial laws in Canada. When a person dies a violent or unexplained death, it is the duty of the coroner to pick a jury and hold a public inquiry to learn how, when, where, and by what means such person came to his demise.

To do this, Coroner McDonald needed an identified body. Assistant Coroner John Quigley elected to climb Mt. Slesse with several amateur mountain climbers. Hauling a rubber sack and a sled, they made slow progress and were halfway to the twin hummocks of snow when a small avalanche roared down the slopes with a thunderous roar. Only a miracle saved Quigley and his amateurs from being swept to their deaths. They immediately retreated to the security of the valley below.

Professional mountain climbers could not be recruited to bring out rotting bodies. There was no place to land a helicopter and besides, the downdrafts were too dangerous for this type of flying machine.

What do do?

Finally, British Columbia and Trans-Canada officials decided it was just too dangerous to attempt to bring the bodies down the mountain at that time of year. They agreed to wait until summer, when the snows would melt and expose the bodies and the danger of avalanches would be less severe. But summer arrived and the snows did not melt.

All concerned—the government, the airline, the families—agreed that it wasn't worth risking human lives to bring down the remains. It was decided to leave the sixty-two victims where they had perished, along with everything else the plane had carried: twenty-seven bags of mail, a thousand pounds of freight and express, baggage, jewels and the money of the passengers, and five hundred pounds of flowers, long withered but the only wreath on the undug graves.

Now came the problem of how to protect the bodies from explorers in search of the money and valuables scattered in the area—especially Kwang Song's $80,000.

The British Columbia provincial government moved fast. Mount Slesse was named a provincial cemetery and mountain climbing on its slopes was banned to eternity, with severe fines and jail terms for any who should violate the prohibition.

Then on the lonely and beautiful forest road leading to the lower slopes of the mountain graveyard, almost hidden in the tall pines on the north side of the tumbling Chilliwack River, a granite monument was erected and on it was inscribed the names of the sixty-two victims. Trans-Canada took some 400 people to the scene exactly one year after the crash and dedicated the monument to all religious faiths while pilots and stewardesses acted as guards of honor for the solemn ceremony.

The Canadian Department of Transport held an inquiry into the crash. But there were no survivors, and the remains of the plane could not be brought down for reassembling and evaluation. So the department's report took a chance at the probable cause: loss of power from the shutting down of one engine and severe thunderstorm turbulence with icing.

Death Shares the Anniversary Flight   7

BEGINNING EARLY IN May, the sun, creeping ever northward over the face of India, directs its hot breath over the surface of the land like a blast furnace and sets up a chain of climatic events that alternately bake and drench the Asian subcontinent.

A canopy of moisture-laden air moves inland from the surrounding seas and is wafted onward and upward by a combination of steady winds from the southeast and the intense heat of the land mass below.

At the same time, a vast quantity of cool, dry air begins to move southward from the chilly land masses of Siberia and Outer Mongolia, reaches the icy barrier of the towering Himalayas, and sweeps over and around the pinnacles of snow and eternal ice, becoming colder and drier in the process.

When this supercooled mass of northern air collides with the hot, moist canopy over the plateaus, the rainy and turbulent season of the monsoon begins. The clash of these two eternal forces is introduced by a symphony of earsplitting crescendos, brilliant electrical pyrotechnics, and torrential downpours of rain.

The massive thunderstorms spawned by these clashes of the air masses are said to be the most violent on the face of the earth. Within the tremendous castles of cumulus clouds erupt nature's most awe-inspiring displays of might and fury.

On the morning of May 2, 1953, the people who lived in the villages and towns along the Ganges River, north and west of Calcutta, began to see the arrival signs of the monsoon season. The wind blew steadily from the southeast. The humidity began rising, and light haze cloaked the fields, cutting visibility to six or seven miles. By ten o'clock the cloud castles began to form and rumble ominously in their birth pains.

The weathermen at Calcutta had forecast thunderstorms in the vicinity of the city for the late afternoon of that day, and the distant rumblings from the sky confirmed their prediction. Shortly after the noon hour, the pilot of an aircraft in the vicinity of the cloud castles radioed the following message to the Air Traffic Control at Calcutta: "Storm developing 24.10 degrees north, 89 degrees east, cumulo-nimbus 3,000 feet, moving southeast direction with very strong vertical updraft."

The Area Control Officer passed the message to the weather office at Calcutta's Dum Dum Airport and then proceeded to "CQ" (a general message to all listening on that frequency) the warning to all aircraft within the Calcutta flight information region. It was repeated several times between 1:13 and 1:17 P.M.

The bulletin was picked up by a BOAC *Comet* jetliner, flying some 30,000 feet over the placid waters of the Bay of Bengal, midway between Rangoon, Burma, and Calcutta. The sleek jet, pride of the British air transport business, was on its scheduled run between Singapore and London and was celebrating the first anniversary of jet passenger travel, inaugurated a year previously by the *Comet*.

Seated in the pilot's position on the left-hand side of the flight deck was veteran Captain Maurice William Haddon, thirty-seven, a pilot-navigator with an incredible 587 hours at the controls of a *Comet* jet. All in all, he had chalked up some 8,700 hours as a pilot since joining the British Overseas Airways Corporation. At the moment that Calcutta issued the weather warning, Capt. Haddon was occupied with the instrumentation of the jet, but he heard the message and asked his radio

The first Comet *flew on July 27, 1949, and went into service with* BOAC *on May 2, 1952. The only* Comets *in service in North America were with the RCAF, as shown here. They were grounded for a considerable time in 1956, after the jets ran into a series of misfortunes.* (De Havilland photo)

officer, Alfred Wood, to copy the forecast and bring it to him for study. His co-pilot, thirty-three-year-old Robert Strange, listened to the routine weather bulletin without comment. He was busy flying the plane. Flight Engineer Albert Gilmore was occupied with the behavior of the four turbojet engines which were effortlessly pushing the *Comet* through the clear, crisp sky at 500 miles an hour.

Radio Officer Wood shoved the weather bulletin into Capt. Haddon's hand, who, in turn, asked for a repeat forecast with an estimate of the time the storm was expected in the Calcutta region. This was extremely important to him, since he would be landing at Dum Dum Airport in less than two hours.

Wood then sent the following signal: "Request forecast time of storm passing Calcutta."

In reply, the Meteorological Office at Dum Dum sent the following message at 2:23 P.M., less than an hour before the *Comet* was to land: "Reference to your signal AAA, the Norwester is expected in the Dum Dum area at 1100 hours GMT."

This would place the thunderstorm in the vicinity of the airport at 4:30 in the afternoon at precisely the same time that Capt. Haddon hoped to be taking off on the next leg in the long, tedious route. This would be to Delhi, capital of India, lying 800 miles northwest of Calcutta, another link in the chain of 6,744 miles between Singapore and London.

Ahead of the *Comet*, lying northward of the long, even curve of the Bengal shoreline, the land was visible beneath a light bluish haze. Further northward, the green flatlands rose sharply to meet the deeply creviced foothills, and beyond this the Himalayas stretched skyward, almost to the height of the jetliner. A score of passengers had just completed a sumptuous luncheon in the two compartments to the rear of the flight deck and were now gazing at the magnificent view from the right side-windows of the airliner. Several were sipping after-dinner cordials being served by steward George Irwin, who had a record of 530 hours on the *Comet*, and by stewardess Patricia Rawlinson, who had chalked up 160 hours on the jet and was a ready source of information to the passengers, unfamiliar at this early stage of jet air travel with the moods and sounds of the tremendous power plants buried in the wings adjacent to the passenger cabin.

At about 2:35 P.M., Capt. Haddon, as was his custom, called for a reduction in the power of the four engines, and the huge airliner began its descent toward the city of Calcutta, some 200 miles ahead. The *Comet* was still in the clear blue sky, sliding lower and lower at 1,000 feet per minute toward the scattered galleons of cumulus clouds that from time to time obscured the hazy ground. The many ribbons of reflected light which marked the mouths of the Ganges River sparkled occasionally through rifts in the clouds. The flight was smooth and delightful.

At three o'clock the beautiful blue and white airliner swept low over the rooftops of Calcutta, the wheels were lowered, and at 3:10 sharp the tires squealed on the concrete runway of Dum Dum Airport and the nose of the *Comet* sliced the brisk southwest ground wind.

Taxiing toward the passenger ramp, Capt. Haddon and others of the flight crew heard the following "special airfield warning" being issued to all aircraft in the vicinity of Dum Dum. "A thunderstorm, accompanied with squalls from the northwest, speed reaching 50 knots, likely at Dum Dum airfield and neighborhood between 5:30 and 6:30 P.M."

A minute later the passengers and crew had departed from the *Comet,* and the fuel trucks moved in to load the wings with kerosene. Capt. Haddon visited the company offices and chatted in the operations room, leaving the flight plan arrangements to his first officer. He rested in his quarters for several minutes and at 4 P.M. decided to make a personal visit to the "Met" office because he was concerned about the special storm warning for the area.

There, Capt. Haddon nodded curtly to Shri Chakaverti, the forecaster on day duty. Then he directed his attention to the maps and the bulletins on the wall. He indicated that he was not so concerned with the weather over the route, as he was with the condition that would exist when he landed at Palam

Airport at Delhi. This would be sometime after six o'clock. The forecaster informed him that the weather at Delhi was excellent: fair skies, a slight ground haziness, with visibility between five and six miles. No sweat for this approach and landing.

The en route weather, however, was both good and bad. For the first 250 miles, to 85 degrees east longitude in the vicinity of the city of Gaya, the reports disclosed an ominous line of scattered thundershowers and moderate turbulence. The high humidity of the day had lowered the base of the clouds to as low as 1,500 feet, while some of the tops were estimated to be as high as 35,000 feet.

The *Comet*'s assigned altitude for the flight to Delhi was 32,000 feet.

Captain Haddon and the forecaster also discussed other conditions along this part of the route. There were a number of cloud groups with bases of 3,000 feet and tops up to 15,000 and 20,000 feet. They would also contain cells of turbulent energy and should be avoided. Between these cloud cities were isolated patches of alto-cumulus and alto-stratus clouds with bases at from 14,000 to 16,000 feet. For the first 250 miles, surface visibility beneath these clouds would range from six to seven miles but would be down to half a mile in showers.

Beyond the 85th meridian, Capt. Haddon was assured that the weather was clear with a few scattered cumulus clouds ranging in height from 3,000 feet above the earth to as high as 18,000 feet. There was a slight amount of dust haze over the ground along the route, but at Palam Airport visibility was a good six miles.

Therefore, with the exception of thunderstorms in the vicinity of Calcutta, the next leg of the *Comet* anniversary flight would be made in clear air, well above the highest of the cloud packs below.

Captain Haddon left the "Met" office, checked operations, and then walked out to the apron, where the *Comet* was receiving its final gallons of fuel. He chatted for a second about the fueling with D. K. Ghosh of the Burma Shell Company, and then made a quick visual inspection of his jet and entered the flight deck of the plane at 4:15 P.M.

The announcement of the flight departure blared over the loudspeaker systems of the Dum Dum terminal. Thirty-seven passengers crowded to the passenger terminal exits to the ramp and began to make their individual ways to the plane.

On the flight deck, Capt. Haddon reviewed the weight list and distribution. His actual take-off weight, he noted, would be 94,327 pounds, well under the maximum allowable of 99,220 pounds for this airport.

He activated the score of switches above his head, while his engineer brought all four De Havilland Ghost 50 engines to life. Passengers were still waving through the circular windows to their friends and to the huge crowd which had gathered at the terminal to watch the sleek jetliner take off. In May 1953 this was still an unusual and thrilling sight.

Captain Haddon wheeled the *Comet* in a tight turn and headed for the warm-up ramp at the northeast corner of the field. He then received the latest weather conditions at the field. ". . . surface winds 180 degrees, 10 knots gusting to 15 knots, visibility seven nautical miles. . . ."

"*Comet* flight cleared for take-off on Runway 19," piped the control tower voice.

Captain Haddon then wheeled the *Comet* in line with Runway 19 left, acknowledged the tower, and signaled with his hand for the flight engineer to bring the four engines to full life. He released the brakes a few seconds later and the jet roared down the runway, lifting off easily after using only two thirds of the concrete strip. The wheels came up and were tucked inside the belly. The captain reported to the tower: "Off at 4:19."

The *Comet* turned gracefully to the right after the take-off and started up through the light haze at 1,000 feet per minute, while the crew changed their radio frequency to Dum Dum Approach at 119.7 megacycles.

The *Comet* then reported to Approach: "Departing Dum Dum on course to Delhi."

Approach Control gave clearance to the jet to climb under visual flight rules and to report when passing 7,500 feet, en route to the 32,000-foot cruising altitude assigned to the flight.

The *Comet* crew was informed that a DC-3 from Delhi was at 7,500 feet and was expected to arrive in fifteen minutes and to keep an eye out for it. There was no reply to this and considerable static noise was building up to help garble communication.

The Approach controller, receiving no reply to his warning concerning the DC-3, called the Area Control Officer, who said he was in touch with the *Comet*. The flight had just reported to him, three minutes after take-off, by wireless: "Departed from Calcutta 1059 hours—estimated time of arrival Palam 1320 hours—climbing to 32,000."

Three minutes later radio operator G. K. Guha Roy, in the Dum Dum communications center, heard the *Comet* calling Delhi radio. He listened as Delhi acknowledged the call, and after an interval he cut in and asked the *Comet* to go ahead with its message, that Delhi was waiting.

There was no answer.

Guha Roy called the aircraft again, repeating that Delhi was "ready and waiting." Only silence greeted this transmission.

It was exactly 4:36 P.M.

Unknown to Dum Dum and Delhi operators, the *Comet* was fighting for its life in the grip of a monsoon thunderstorm—the storm which had been so accurately predicted to its commander.

During its climb, and six minutes after its take-off, the jet airliner encountered the storm, known to Indian weather forecasters as a "nor'wester squall." Such storms are well known to airline pilots flying in monsoon weather—particularly to Capt. Haddon, who had flown these routes on many occasions.

A typical "nor'wester" consists of a giant column of rising hot air covering an immense area, thirty to forty square miles, during its formative stages. As the warm air rises, it increases in velocity to upwards of fifty miles an hour. Sometimes, many cells of varying intensity mix with the clouds and churn upward and downward within the clouds. The mature stage of the storm starts with a heavy downpour of rain with accompanying downdrafts of between fifteen and fifty miles an hour.

Dangerous lenticular clouds are often buried within other cloud structures, as is shown in this striking photograph taken over the Western Rockies. (Photo by James Yarnell)

On encountering such a situation, standard operating procedure called for an immediate reduction in power and for the pilot to take over the control of the jet from the automatic pilot. This is exactly what Capt. Haddon did. He was trying to maintain the attitude of the aircraft while his co-pilot and engineer kept watch on the air-speed indicators, controlling the throttles so as not to exceed the specified limit of maneuvering speed.

Suddenly, in the blackness of the turbulence broken only by the blinding cascades of lightning bolts, the *Comet* flew into a violent downdraft. The nose went down. The huge jet shuddered in anguish. The altimeter dropped alarmingly. The air speed increased. The pilot called for less power and reacted instantly by pulling back on the control column. The *Comet* responded, but at that precise second an elevator failed. This failure imposed a heavy download on the wings.

The passengers and crew were slammed into their seats by the violence of the maneuvers. They could see the wings flapping wildly. Then came the sickening and heart-stopping sight as one wing and then the other snapped.

One of the wings careened rearward into the rudder assembly, shearing it like a knife cutting through soft cheese. The other wing reared against the fuselage, slicing through into the passenger compartment. The fuel cells, thus ruptured, exploded with blinding violence and the *Comet* plunged into a vertical dive.

A lonely shepherd, two field workers in a rice paddy, a farmer and a railroad station master were the only eyewitnesses to the frightful disaster.

Working at their respective jobs along a straight line some five miles in length, the four men had paused in their labors to stare at the gathering storm. As the black churning squall line bore down upon them, Kishori Mohan Chakravati, tending his flock near the village of Jagalgori, the northernmost village along the five-mile line, prayed that the lightning would not strike near by and panic his sheep.

Narayan Chandra Ghosh, in a paddy several hundred yards
from the shepherd, and Chandra Bidhu Singh Ray, in another
paddy some distance from the others and near the tiny village
of Thanashampur, laughed at the coming of the rains. It meant
food and work.

Tenant farmer Avash Chandra Singh Ray, at the village of
Mahishnan, rushed from his cottage to secure his cattle, keeping his eyes on the fast approaching squall line.

Karuna Kinker Mukerjee, station master at the Martin Railway Line depot at the village of Jangipuri located halfway
down the five-mile line and slightly west of it, was concerned
that the storm would wipe out communications with the other
stops along the line—the same as every monsoon since he could
remember. "This is a bad one," he muttered.

The shepherd Kishori was the first to see the bright object
falling like a meteor toward the ground where he was standing.
Paralyzed by fright, he stared in terror and disbelief as the
fiery, exploding, roaring aircraft rushed closer and closer like a
demon with gaping jaws of hellfire.

The field worker Ghosh, transfixed, stared with quaking fear
at the frightening and unexplainable development high above
his head. He had been looking into the very maw of the storm,
grateful for the rain that was cascading down his face and over
his scantily clad body, when he saw a strange orange-colored
flash. It continued brighter and closer with every second and
he screamed in terror as he thought the awful object was going
to strike him. The *Comet* crashed with a roar like thunder into
a nearby ravine, which the Indians call a nullah and which is
similar to the dry arroyos of the southwest United States. The
impact knocked Ghosh to the ground.

The shepherd Kishori, standing not far away, also was
hurled to the earth. Bits of flaming wreckage showered the
area. Kishori, thereupon, headed for the village, his eyes
dilated by fear, his feet moving like pistons.

At Inchagur, at the southerly end of the five-mile line, the
Comet's port elevator and top wing skin fell to the wet ground.
At the next village north, Angada, the outboard rear engine

panel fell in flames. Pieces of the bottom part of the wing and shreds of fuselage also impacted here. Then further along the line of villages, Kapar Pur, Dingal Hati, Khulsani, Santosh, Ghanshampur, Raspur, and so on to Jagalhati, bits and pieces of broken metal, cushions, burning fabric, and other items drew a straight line of evidence leading to the main wreckage itself.

Despite the deluge from the monsoon, the wreckage burned until almost everything had been consumed.

At 4:40 P.M. and again at 4:54, Dum Dum Area Control, unaware of the tragedy, sent out special weather bulletins which were given to the communications section for transmission to the *Comet*. These dealt with the weather at Gaya and Delhi. The communication radio tried to pass along this information but of course was unable to raise the flight. Communications was not worried, believing that the *Comet* had cut off its radio because of the heavy static. This silence was not known to Dum Dum Area Control, which presumed that normal communication with the *Comet* was being maintained.

At 5:29 P.M., Palam Airport at Delhi asked Calcutta Traffic Control if it was in touch with the *Comet*, as a "Dangermet" (a weather bulletin warning of danger) was being held up at Palam. As a result of this, Calcutta Control checked with communications and learned that no message had been received from the aircraft since the one at 4:32 P.M. Only then was it realized that all contact with the *Comet* had ceased almost a full hour before.

Near panic reigned for several minutes as airport personnel checked to ascertain whether or not the flight had reported to any of the many agencies concerned with its progress. When only shocked silence greeted all inquiries, Area Control sent out a general alarm.

To say that officials of BOAC were shocked to numbness would be putting it mildly. It was the second fatal crash for the *Comets*, the other having occurred in nearby Pakistan, killing all aboard.

The locating of the wreckage, some twenty-two miles northwest of Dum Dum, was delayed many hours. Area Control wirelessed all airports in the district and then waited agonizing hours for the messages to return. The *Comet* was to have landed at 6:50 P.M. at Palam, and five minutes after this time the communications personnel at Dum Dum were asked to signal Palam in the hope that the aircraft had landed safely, its silence to be explained by the fury of the storm and the disruption of radio signals.

"Aircraft has not landed," reported Palam.

Distress action was immediately taken. All police outposts were advised by wireless of the missing airliner, and patrols were hastily recruited. All military headquarters were alerted and the Chief Secretary of West Bengal joined in the concern and personally passed on the information to all districts in this vast area between Calcutta and Delhi. The police at Gaya were asked to institute a search, as this was a storm area where officials thought the plane might have gone down. Gaya was 250 miles away. No one could conceive that the *Comet* had expired six minutes after take-off. Had it not been for the clouds, the plane would have been clearly visible from the airport tower at so short a distance.

Meanwhile, after the frightful shock had diminished somewhat, the lonely shepherd Kishori reached the village of Jagalgori and informed the local Darogo of the explosion. He, in turn, ran to a neighboring village to inform subinspector of police Manoranjan Dey of the crash. This police officer had been visiting another policeman and both cycled to the closest road approach to the nullah, which had been turned into a roaring torrent by the rising water. All the while the deluge of rain continued, almost three inches having fallen since the advent of the storm.

Subinspector Dey found two parts of the aircraft. They were still burning. He pedaled to the railway station to send the alarm to Calcutta. "Tell them that two airplanes have collided," he gasped. But the main telegraph wire had been broken by the storm and the agent was able to move the message only to the next station, which in turn would move it on to the next, if it was open at the time, and so on down the line toward Calcutta.

At dawn on May 3, two Royal Indian Air Force aircraft accompanied by a BOAC *York* transport took off from Dum Dum to search for the missing airliner. Shortly afterwards, a railway station agent in Calcutta received the message from Jagalgori and passed it on to the nearest district police station, called Lallbazar. The latter immediately called Area Control at Dum Dum.

This was the report no one wanted to hear and yet for which all had been waiting. Area Control directed the search aircraft to Jagalgori and within half an hour the disaster was confirmed and first-aid teams and investigators headed out to the country-side to probe the remains. Of the forty-three persons on board, only the badly burned bodies of forty were recovered. The fire had consumed almost the entire jetliner and only intense inves-tigation by a team of experts would find the cause of the in-flight breakup.

It was evident that a violent thunderstorm had caused the crash. This was confirmed in the probe which followed.

Why had this occurred? Was the pilot at fault? Was the *Comet*, already a victim of other disasters, not structurally sound?

First of all, the investigators took a keen look at the per-formance of the ill-fated plane itself, checking back through the months it had been in service with BOAC. They found that the *Comet* had already been subjected to spine-chilling dam-age due in part to flying in turbulent weather conditions in an area not far from where it finally ended its career.

On July 28, 1952, a short time after it was certified as being airworthy, this *Comet* had been operating between Karachi and Delhi when it ran into turbulence created, again, by the southwest monsoon. Some 7 G's were recorded on its delicate instruments. Ground checking disclosed a popped rivet in the port main wheel and a blister on the top wing surface, as well as other damage.

Then, three weeks later, a major forging on the right-hand side of the plane had cracked.

Besides these two troubles, the *Comet* also had suffered a fire in a radio unit while flying from Rome to London, and on another occasion had undershot a landing at Beirut, causing considerable damage to its belly.

It would almost seem that this *Comet* was doomed from the start.

Next, what about the pilot?

Maurice William Haddon was born on June 21, 1916. He had started flying in 1935 and continued training with single- and twin-engine aircraft until December 1938, when he had joined BOAC as a probationary second officer. As the years passed, he went through the long list of titles and subtitles that finally got him his senior captaincy, first class, in February 1951. From the moment he joined BOAC, he had flown all through Europe, Africa, the Middle East, and the Far East. He had flown just about every type of passenger aircraft known to the trade.

During his BOAC career he had had three accidents. In 1939 he had overshot on landing at the city of Shoreham, England, in his Lockheed 14, but no responsibility for the accident was placed on him. In 1944, a belly landing at Jiwani had brought him commendation for his exceptional airmanship from the company and the British Air Ministry.

On April 23, 1952, in another *Comet*, he had landed heavily at Khartoum, causing considerable damage to the aircraft, and had been admonished.

But this latter incident could happen to any pilot. All in all, Capt. Haddon was, without doubt, an excellent pilot with years of experience in flying under all sorts of conditions.

Then why did he fly into a monsoon thunderstorm, when he had been warned on several occasions that the storm was on his route?

He was first warned of the thunderstorm forecasts while flying from Rangoon to Calcutta and he had even gone so far as to ask for more details on the situation. Then, on his arrival at Dum Dum Airport, he had personally talked with the forecaster, who recalled: "It seems that the Captain was more anxious about the weather at the terminal [Palam-Delhi] than about the en route weather."

Did this mean that Capt. Haddon was not as concerned with the weather warning as he should have been?

The special storm warning bulletin was also received at Dum Dum by Edward Wheeler, the station officer of BOAC, and he personally had handed the warning to Capt. Haddon. It specifically mentioned that gusts up to 50 knots an hour could be expected in the northeast squall line that would accompany the predicted thunderstorm. Wheeler had accompanied Haddon to the "Met" office for the weather briefing.

According to the BOAC manual, the weather minimums for *Comets* at Dum Dum were as follows: "Subject to the ILS and the non-directional beacon being serviceable, the take-off conditions at Dum Dum on Runway 19 is cloud base of 300 feet and visibility 1,000 yards."

Investigators wished, when they arrived at the city, they could find another plane which had been flying in the same region, at the same time as the *Comet*, under almost identical circumstances.

In this desire, they were indeed fortunate. After the *Comet* had climbed off the runway and disappeared into the haze, Captain C. J. Vlotman, of Royal Dutch Airlines (KLM), had wheeled his giant *Constellation* onto the same runway, revved up the engines, received his routing to Karachi, and had taken off less than thirty minutes behind the ill-fated *Comet*.

Captain Vlotman had received the same weather information as had Capt. Haddon. He encountered the thunderstorm between twelve and fifteen miles from the airport, and, changing direction slightly, he flew at 4,500 feet, keeping his altitude down because he had been specifically warned by the forecaster of cumulo-nimbus clouds on his route. Vlotman flew east and under the storm without incident and then climbed to 20,000 feet for the remainder of the flight. His testimony was incorporated into the minutes of the investigation.

In summing up the evidence, James Herbert Lett, investigating officer of the Accidents Investigation Branch of the Ministry of Civil Aviation, London, attributed the cause of the crash to complete structural failure in the air. Examination of the wreckage showed no signs of sabotage, lightning damage, faulty workmanship, defective material or power plant failure.

The probable cause of the structural failure was due either to the severe gusts in the thunderstorm or to overcontrolling or loss of control by the pilot while flying in the storm.

The report, one of the most comprehensive in the history of flying accidents, pointed out that Capt. Haddon was in full possession of the weather briefings and had been given all the relevant information for his flight. The investigation found that the captain was "well qualified and had considerable experience of weather conditions on this route."

"He was therefore fully competent to judge the weather forecast en route and the warnings given, and make up his mind whether to take off or not.

"It would not be right to accuse him of any imprudence taking off in spite of the warning," said the official investigation report.

And that was that.

They buried the victims where they fell and nothing disturbs their resting place except the vibrations of the earth below the monsoon thunderstorms that begin every May as regularly as clockwork, building tremendous anvils that dwarf the towering Himalayas to the north.

Heads, You Win — Tails, You Lose 8

THERE HAVE BEEN countless occasions when pilots have flown
into severe weather conditions without having prior knowledge
of the weather along the route. Faulty forecasting has been
responsible for a few such surprises, but most often the situation has been due to the fact that the flights were in lonely
regions where weather forecasts were often meager or unavail-
able altogether.

On a blustery and rain-swept afternoon, fifty passengers
trooped into a Douglas DC-6B operated by Trans-Ocean Airlines and homeward bound from Wake Island to California.
A refueling stop was scheduled at Honolulu, Hawaii. Many
passengers were members of families of construction workers
heading home for Christmas and winter vacations. There were
forty-one men and women and nine children on the flight.

The flight was called *The Royal Hawaiian*. The pilot was
Captain William Word of San Leandro, California. His co-pi-
lots, already at their places in the flight deck, were Herbert
Hudson of Mountain View, California, and Len. H. Norvell of
San Jose.

For these long flights, the DC-6B carried a flight engineer as
well as a navigator. They were George Haskamp and John Hay.
For this particular run, a student engineer-trainee was aboard.
He was Paul Yedwabnick and he was on his first Trans-Ocean
training flight.

The stewardess for the trip was Louise Downing of Los Angeles and her assistant was the steward-purser, H. H. Sargent.

With this crew of eight, *The Royal Hawaiian* was expected to take off from Wake Island and arrive at Honolulu in 12 hours' time. Unfortunately, the weather over the route was to interfere with their flight plan.

Captain Word, a veteran pilot, knew that flying the Pacific was unlike any other flying in the world. The weather reports were meager and often just guesswork. Vast cold fronts would sweep out of Siberia, cross over the coasts north of Japan, and roll eastward and southward over the lonely reaches of the ocean and their discovery was often by accident. Sometimes the weather ships, few and far between, would be able to predict the movement of these turbulent frontal systems. But, more often, the fronts would move unobserved for days, their paths being unpredictable because of the lack of land-based or sea-based stations to plot their movements and their pressure patterns. During the war, the United States actually had set up a secret weather base in the Gobi Desert just to track these storm movements and to help predict the weather for long-range reconnaissance and bombing missions.

Captain Word knew all these things. Today, his flight from Guam had been reasonably good. Just a little rain and cloud. He hoped the rest of the trip would be as comfortable.

At 5:58 P.M. sharp, he took the DC-6B off the Wake runway and pointed her nose in the direction of Hawaii and in the direction of the high cloud castles illuminated in the rays of the setting sun.

The Royal Hawaiian climbed steadily upward at 500 feet per minute until it reached the altitude of 15,000 feet which Capt. Word had decided would be the best altitude for the trip, considering wind and cloud conditions.

At 10:29 P.M., the flight reported its position as 325 miles east of Wake. This was the last message ever received from the plane.

During the night, Air Traffic controllers at Honolulu became alarmed at the failure of the flight to report its position. Wake

Island operators were asked if they had received any word of the flight's position and they all reported negatively. All the controllers could do was to await the dawn, when *The Royal Hawaiian* was due to arrive at Honolulu, because radio messages often failed to get through stormy areas and sometimes radio transmitters broke down.

But dawn came and there was no sight of the giant aircraft with the fifty-eight persons aboard. Now overdue and certainly out of fuel, the flight was listed as missing. At once ships and planes moved out into the Pacific from Guam, Wake, Hawaii, Midway, and Kwajalein on one of the most comprehensive search missions in aviation history. The Coast Guard weather ship *French* moved in to assist, and twelve Navy P2V's were designated as the air liaison force.

Late in the first day's search, one of the P2V's sighted an oil slick, 320 miles due east of Wake, but oncoming darkness prevented a closer look. The next morning a tremendous fleet of ships and planes descended on the area and began a series of sweeps back and forth, back and forth, over hundreds of square miles, as, all the while, the winds grew stronger, the seas mounted, and rain squalls cut down visibility.

During these sweeps, two more oil slicks were observed from the air and vessels concentrated on this one spot. Suddenly, from the crow's-nest of one of the search vessels, two small white objects were sighted. These were the bodies of two children, and they were immediately retrieved by a Navy transport. Closer searching of the adjacent waters turned up life rafts, half submerged, and then more bodies. These bodies had been mangled by sharks, and searchers actually saw one body drawn under the surface by sharks, not to reappear again. Three badly burned bodies were recovered. Two others were horribly mangled, apparently by an explosion. All four of the flight's life rafts were recovered.

In the floating debris, searchers picked up shoes, clothing and luggage. Not recovered were any of the crew, nor the body of the nervous passenger who had been rushing home to attend his brother's funeral in Morehouse, Mo. The funeral had been postponed for eight days awaiting his arrival. Now it would proceed without him.

Investigation by the U. S. Civil Aeronautics Board (CAB) revealed that the flight had made its last radio contact with the outside world at 8:29, Guam central time, reporting its position and its altitude at 15,000 feet between cloud layers. Although the probable cause could not be determined, analysis of the weather indicated the possibility that the flight had entered a thunderstorm. There was no other reasonable explanation for the disaster. It has been officially listed by the CAB as an accident involving thunderstorm activity.

Then, too, there have been cases on record of forecasters who have not been able to warn pilots of severe weather conditions along the air corridors, having learned too late of the bad weather and finding it impossible to alert the airplane crews.

Controllers in the airport tower of Waterloo, Iowa, tried in vain to reach a Braniff International Airways DC-3 on Sunday afternoon, August 22, 1954, to warn the plane that an ugly thunderstorm was in its flight path.

The two-engined aircraft operating as Flight 152, a Braniff milk run from Memphis to Minneapolis, had taken off from the runway at Waterloo at 4:30 P.M. And at 4:45 the controllers were trying to raise the crew through the gathering static.

Flying the DC-3 were pilots A. W. Pickering and W. B. Wilde. There were nineteen passengers aboard, almost a full load in the 21-passenger aircraft. It was a dependable aircraft operated by a dependable company that had not had a fatal accident since 1939.

Fifteen minutes after the take-off, the aircraft was in the grip of a blinding thunderstorm. A witness saw it enter a light spot and disappear in the storm. One mile beyond this, its smoldering wreckage was observed. Witnesses saw it bounce 500 feet upward after being dashed to the ground in hail showers and violent wind. After this bouncing, it mushed into a sodden farm field, ten miles west of Mason City, Iowa.

Miraculously, the DC-3 did not catch fire and explode. As a

This Braniff DC-3 tangled with an August thunderstorm near Mason City, Iowa. (Civil Aeronautics Board photo)

result, only eleven persons died. Investigation by the CAB showed the aircraft struck the ground in a level attitude. Interrogation of witnesses revealed that it had been as low as 400 feet over the terrain when the pilot sought to go into the light area beneath the storm. But the violent downdrafts, associated with all thunderstorms, probably caught the aircraft and literally dashed it into the ground.

There are occasions when pilots see the thunderstorms and attempt to circumvent them, as they have been advised to do. There is a case on record in which two aircraft approached the same storm and both pilots swung away to avoid it. One succeeded. The other didn't.

United Air Lines' DC-3 flight from Cleveland to Chicago was on course and on time that evening of Saturday, April 28, 1951. There would be an intermediate landing at the airport at Fort Wayne, Indiana, to discharge Eastern passengers for South Bend and other communities in the vicinity.

At the controls was Captain E. K. Swallow of Hinsdale, Ill., veteran pilot for United. By his side sat co-pilot H. R. Miller of Chicago, and back in the passenger compartment stewardess Beverly Ellis was taking care of eight passengers, one an FBI agent and three others nurses bound for South Bend after completing psychiatric courses in Cleveland.

Captain Swallow radioed his position to the Fort Wayne airport tower and was given landing instructions as he circled south of the airport for a routine approach. At the same time, another DC-3, operated by Trans World Airlines (TWA) came into the traffic pattern and both planes moved toward the airport, known as Baer Field.

But also descending on the airport was a vicious thunderstorm, with a line squall typical of all cold front thunderstorms, and it was moving a great deal faster than the Weather Bureau at Fort Wayne had predicted. The pilots of both planes realized they could not land safely with the storm moving toward them in such a rapid manner and they elected to change course. Capt. Swallow radioed the airport that he was turning east to circumvent the storm. The TWA pilot did likewise. It was light enough for both pilots to see each other's aircraft, and they were careful to keep well apart.

At this moment winds in the tumbling squall line were upwards of eighty-five miles an hour and they struck the airport with all the fury of a tropical hurricane. Rain and hail slammed against the airport tower windows, but that didn't hinder the controllers from seeing the horrifying sight of the next few seconds.

Captain Swallow had not managed to clear his aircraft from below the dangerous overhang of the thunderstorm. As a result his DC-3 was caught in a severe downdraft and smashed in a level attitude right into the ground. A tremendous explosion followed and the orange glow was seen from the control tower. Ambulances and fire reels were immediately dispatched to the scene, but the heavy rainfall had made the plowed fields impassable and the rescuers stood helpless while the flames consumed the plane. National Guard jeeps were brought to the scene to assist firemen and rescue crews at the crash site, but the heat of the fire was so intense they were unable to retrieve the bodies.

Meanwhile, the TWA pilot, noticing the extent of the storm and the severity of the squall line, kept on turning eastward and finally headed for Toledo, Ohio, where he landed safely with his passengers. There he awaited the storm's passing.

Investigation of the tragedy turned up a witness. Henry Facks was a farmer who, while caught in the storm, had heard the airliner above him. He estimated the height of the aircraft to have been about 1,000 feet. He saw it lifted up, flipped over, and then lazily mashed downward into the ground.

The time by his watch had been just 7:30 P.M., Central standard time.

Thus ended the United flight to Fort Wayne, victim of a local thunderstorm that could be clearly seen and which, in fact, the pilot had tried to avoid.

Many air disasters occurred in the days before weather radar when forecasting was often sketchy. In many instances local thunderstorms which were expected to be brief and unspectacular would grow in size with unpredictable severity and turbulence.

Such a case happened at Hanford City, California, on November 4, 1944. It was the same night that British bombers were raiding Cologne; the Allies were driving into Holland, and the Budapest defenses were crumbling. Perhaps with all these exciting victories of the war, the tragedy was over and forgotten in one brief day.

The plane was a DC-3 operated by TWA. At the lethal altitude of 10,000 feet, it ran smack into a violent thunderstorm with all the pyrotechnics of the heavens lighting the sky around it. But it didn't travel very far into the storm. Captain A. T. Bethel and First Officer G. E. Smith attempted to control the pitching aircraft, loaded to capacity with twenty-one passengers and one stewardess. The crew were all from the Los Angeles area.

The DC-3, unable to stand the pounding, gave up a wing. A violent explosion of high-octane fuel followed as the tanks ruptured. The aircraft came apart in the air. Bodies were scattered over a wide area. One witness, A. A. Avila, saw bodies falling from a great height and said they looked like birds. Another witness described the scene as "looking like a battlefield."

Pilots will long remember the Trans-Canada Air Lines captain, flying a DC-4M-2 from Winnipeg to Toronto during a summer night several years ago, who noticed the increasing frequency of lightning ahead of him at his level of 19,000 feet. As he moved closer to the storm, which appeared to be centered over Lake Superior, he became aware that lightning was gradually building up to the south of him and also to the north, and in the flashes he could see the towering castles of cumulus.

Danger on three sides.

He decided to return to Winnipeg. He swung the DC-4M-2 in a half circle and headed westward. Lightning now appeared on his return route and radio reports confirmed that the storm

This is the sad remains of the TWA DC-3 that flew into a thunder-storm over Hanford, California, in 1944. (Civil Aeronautics Board photo)

was gathering strength and closing inexorably around him like a giant vise. He was in the eye of a tremendous series of previously unrelated thunderstorms that were now joining forces faster than he could fly between them.

What to do?

He had forty-four passengers aboard. He would have to get down and out of it. But there were no airports anywhere near him, the nearest being at Fort William, almost 150 miles to the east, and the other at Winnipeg, 200 miles west. The route south to Minneapolis was closed by the storms also.

Taking out his maps of this lonely vicinity, he began to study the emergency field locations and found one almost underneath his present position. His mind made up, he took the giant plane down through the gathering cumulus clouds and without the aid of his radio direction finder located the lonely emergency strip. It was unlighted. It was gravel surfaced and only 3,500 feet long.

But he landed his aircraft on the field safe and sound. The next day the passengers were driven to a regular airport some distance away because he could not get the giant plane off such a short runway while it was loaded.

His decision probably saved the lives of his passengers.

Sunday, August 29, 1948, has long since been forgotten as the date of one of the worst thunderstorm disasters in the early history of U. S. commercial flying.

Involved was Northwest Airlines, an airline that has suffered considerably over the years from the Anvil of the Gods. The plane was a Martin 2-0-2, a plane which provided Northwest with not a few headaches during its early years of operation. The location was near Winona, Minnesota, where the Mississippi River winds its lazy muddy course between the bluffs of green and the fields of ripened corn. The day was warm and humid and weathermen called it unstable. Building up in the late afternoon sky were the familiar anvils of the thunderstorms. One of the storms was destined to play with the Martin 2-0-2 like a child bouncing a rubber ball. And the Martin 2-0-2 was just not built to take this kind of treatment.

The drama began at Chicago's busy Midway Airport. Captain Robert Johnson of St. Paul, and co-pilot Dave Brenner of Minneapolis boarded the 2-0-2 at 5:30 P.M. for the nonstop flight to Minneapolis, where they were due to land at 7:30 P.M. The flight would travel at 7,000 feet over the lush harvestland of Illinois and Wisconsin and would cross over the Mississippi River near La Crosse, Wisconsin, and continue in a northwestward direction over the mighty river to the twin cities of Minneapolis and St. Paul. It was a routine milk run for the pilots of Northwest.

As Capt. Johnson and Brenner talked with Air Traffic Control, stewardess Mary Ungs of Minneapolis checked thirty-three adult passengers aboard. It was a dinner flight and she knew she would have her hands full. There was also one infant on the flight and that meant warming the baby bottle and the baby foods. But all this was part of the routine and Mary Ungs was a competent stewardess who loved her job.

The flight was cleared by Departure Control, and Captain Johnson took the heavily loaded plane off the runway at 4:50 P.M. (CDT) and pointed the nose of the craft toward the northwest.

For the first three quarters of the trip, the flight was uneventful, but the plane was traveling closer and closer to the thunderstorms which were building up on its path—thunderstorms created by the hot sun's causing the air to rise to great heights where it soon cooled, giving up its moisture, which condensed and started falling as rain and hail.

At 5:55 P.M. the pilot sent the following message: "Severe thunderstorms in this area . . . we're at 7,000." This was the last message from the flight.

The next episode occurred on the ground. Mrs. Charles Guenther, a farmer's wife, had been shopping in the town of Winona that afternoon and was anxious to return to the farm and prepare dinner. Her husband, at the wheel of the car, was concentrating on the road ahead while she watched the panorama of the land and the gathering thunderstorm building its castles of black and blue over the river between Winona, which she just left, and the town of Fountain City on the Wisconsin side of the river.

As Mrs. Guenther watched, she saw a frightening sight . . . an airliner rolling over and over like a barrel. Parts of the plane were breaking away and falling to the ground. The rain was now pouring furiously, but she could still see the falling aircraft. Her husband, startled by her frightened cries, stopped the car and ran out to watch. He too saw the plane rolling over and over. Then it crashed with a thunderous roar on a ridge of land just ahead of them, near the village of Sutters Ridge.

Parking their car at the edge of the roadway, they tried to find the broken aircraft but in vain. Then they called police. The first officers to reach the scene through the storm-lashed area started up the bluffs. They came upon a piece of the aircraft's wing. Then the tail. Then the decapitated body of a man. He was lying in a flooded creek.

The officers climbed higher and found three more bodies. Next was the body of a young woman, nude, her clothes torn off by the force of the impact. But she was still clinging to her purse. They reached the main wreckage, a pile of twisted junk. In the nose was the pilot and back in the broken fuselage were the bodies of ten others. One woman was holding her baby in her arms.

The rest of the bodies and the rest of the Martin 2-0-2 was found scattered over seven miles of bluff land. It took searchers several days to account for all bodies and aircraft parts.

Confusion reigned for some time over the number of persons on the flight, but it was finally established that thirty-seven perished—three crew members and thirty-four passengers.

Investigation disclosed that the aircraft had entered the thunderstorm where the turbulence was severe and that a structural failure resulted, originating in the wing panel attachment fitting. The aircraft then broke apart in the air, with the resulting appalling loss of life.

On and on the storms of the world take their toll in the skies like a giant wheel of misfortune, sometimes as broad as a hurricane and sometimes as narrow as a tornado, but with moods which are often predictable and visible to the bellicose mortals who defy them and the more timid ones who respect them.

On April 6, 1958, a Capital Airlines *Viscount* stalled and crashed while approaching Midland City airport in Michigan with forty-four passengers and a crew of three. Investigation of this disaster showed that the flight had made a steep turn, with contributing factors to the crash being the gusty wind associated with a thunderstorm, and possible accretion of ice.

While on the subject of ice for a moment, there is on record the flight of an American Airlines DC-6 out of Dallas on May 25, 1949. The aircraft passed through a line of thunderstorms and penetrated the area which the pilot believed offered the least thunderstorm activity. The aircraft proceeded into this dangerous region at reduced air speed. Exactly two minutes after entering the clouds, the air speed increased very rapidly and a heavy blast of hail struck the plane, breaking both windshields and inflicting substantial damage on the fuselage and wings. The pilot immediately made a left turn on a southeasterly heading, and in three minutes the flight broke into the clear. It then returned to Dallas and made a safe landing. No one was injured.

On June 13, 1947, a Pennsylvania Central DC-4 crashed in a storm at Leesburg, Virginia, and took fifty people to oblivion.

On January 16, 1959, an Australian Airlines *Commando* crashed in a violent thunderstorm while flying over Mar Del Plata, Argentina, and fifty-one persons died.

On June 26, 1959, a TWA *Super Constellation* crashed in a storm at Milan, Italy, and sixty-eight persons lost their lives.

By this time all these horrible disasters have a familiar ring.

The evidence points to a single conclusion: Thunderstorms can be lethal to commercial flying. The lessons learned from the past and the progress in electronics and in machines have made little difference. The forces of nature have not diminished and it isn't likely that they will.

Radar 9

THE WORD "radar" itself is an acronym formed from the words: *Radio Detection and Ranging.*

Radar is a system which utilizes high-frequency pulses of radio waves beamed into the atmosphere at the speed of light. These echo back from solid objects, which are then illuminated on a screen. The interval of time between the sending of the signals and their return to the screen determines the distance of the object under study and surveillance.

Since radio signals echo from raindrops because of their solid nuclei, radar can easily locate the densest bands of precipitation. It can also examine dangerous cloud formations to find turbulent cells of energy, and search other cloud formations which could conceal hail and tornadoes and hurricanes.

Radar is installed in commercial aircraft for the prime purpose of locating turbulence so that the pilot can avoid it. It can also be used to detect the presence of other aircraft or ground obstruction, and, in some cases, can be used as an extremely accurate altimeter.

In view of the fact that there is a near-miss every three minutes in the air space over the United States, radar is doubly important. A near-miss is described officially as the situation in which two planes come so close to each other that a collision is avoided only by one pilot taking immediate evasive action.

Mid-air collisions occur more often than realized. During the past twenty-five years in the United States, there have been some 450 collisions officially reported and investigated.

Many times this number in near collisions have never been reported and it would be spine-chilling, to say the least, to be aware of the near-misses that have occured at night or in clouds, unknown to the pilots of either of the aircraft involved. As air speed increases and more planes utilize the airways, the danger of collision multiplies enormously and thus the use of radar in the control of air traffic is exceedingly important. Without radar, there would be utter chaos in today's crowded airways.

Radar used for weather detecting purposes, whether in the air or on the ground, can easily disclose frontal systems hundreds of miles away. It can quickly identify thunderstorms and squall lines, and their images can be magnified in such a manner that pilots and ground weather observers can actually look into the very heart of storms and determine their potential danger.

Basically, from the standpoint of equipment involved, radar consists of four essential ingredients:

1. A transmitter designed to send out the radio waves.
2. An antenna which concentrates the waves into an outgoing directional beam and receives the rebounding echo reflected from any solid object or objects in the beam's path.
3. A receiver designed to detect the infinitesimal portion of the radio pulse that is echoed back.
4. A device for measuring the time interval between the pulse and the returning echo in millionths of a second, and graphically portraying this information on a small circular screen.

The echoes appear as "blips" on the screen, the time interval between the blips providing the method for arriving at the range.

The direction of the object to be studied is determined by revolving the radar's antenna to a position where the echoes appear to be the strongest.

This is part of a typical instrument flight room at a large terminal. The two men on the right are FAA traffic controllers, monitoring surveillance radarscopes, which show aircraft for 30 miles around the airport. The controller at the left is seated at the Precision Approach Radar, giving the pilot all the advisory information he'll need for landing. (Civil Aeronautics Board photo)

Airplanes and thunderheads both appear on this scope during a thunderstorm over central Florida. The large white spaces are storm centers; the little dots represent an airplane about to enter a thunderhead. (U. S. Air Force photo)

This is the Ground Control Center of the Air Traffic Control at New York City. There are 2,370 landings and take-offs in the New York area every day of the year, and trouble usually occurs only in bad weather. Airlines and government agencies as well as pilots are continually looking for greater safety aids at busy airports.

When two antennas are used, the time lag between signals received by them will give the height of the object under study.

When properly used, radar provides a clear-cut televised map of what lies ahead of the aircraft. It can also sweep a full circle, and does so at airports and at Weather Bureaus.

The circular screen, sometimes referred to as an indicator, is a cathode ray tube of sufficient size and clarity to be clearly visible from the pilot's position. This tube acts much like the picture tube in a home television set. Pulses of light flash across the screen, the periods of pulsation equaling the frequency of the radio signals. Yet they appear to the human eye as a single beam of light.

Actually, this single beam is a glowing line of lights that sweeps around the screen like the illuminated second hand of a clock. Since this beam sweeps continuously, the blip, or image, is continuously and regularly reinforced, often enough to make the objects under surveillance stand out with fantastic sharpness and clarity.

It is almost unbelievable that such a phenomenal discovery should have gathered dust for so long a time. Radar was discovered in the early Thirties by British scientists and became operational in 1935 with an impressive degree of accuracy and dependability. But it took the Battle of Britain to bring it to full blossom. Installed along the Channel coast, the radar antennas scanned the eastern skies night and day to pick up German raiders while they were still over the Continent. This early warning not only saved millions of lives by driving Britons into air raid shelters long in advance of the devastating onslaughts, but also permitted the harried Royal Air Force to concentrate its fighter planes along the path of the raiders, thus saving tired pilots for important radar-determined defense action and relieving them of monotonous and fatiguing hunt-and-strike patrols.

But if radar helped England and her Allies as a defensive measure of the first magnitude, it also assisted offensively. The Royal Air Force was able to strike at German targets under cover of clouds and darkness with great accuracy. The Royal

Navy was able to attack German surface vessels at night and in foggy weather, as well as to conduct raids along the enemy coast without fear of aerial attacks or bombardment by powerful shore batteries.

As the Second World War progressed, so did radar. Skilled British operators were soon able to tell the direction of various German bombing formations with such proficiency that hundreds of raids were broken up and thousands of airplanes destroyed before they reached their target. Meanwhile England was working feverishly to build up her Royal Air Force.

Strange as it may seem, the introduction of radar to North America was anything but enthusiastic. Had it not been for a high-ranking Canadian Government official it might have been shelved for the entire war on this side of the Atlantic.

When hostilities began in September 1939, the governments of Canada and Great Britain asked the University of Toronto to institute a crash course of study in the newfangled gadget which the British called radar. A small group of brilliant students were drafted into the course. One of the graduates, Herbert ("Terry") Birtchell, who had recently joined the Royal Canadian Navy, was transferred to England and to the Royal Navy as fleet radar officer for the Mediterranean Theatre. At Oran and Casablanca, radar operated by this young officer proved its worth in the naval attacks on shore installations. After the victory, Birtchell, now a commander, was whisked across the Atlantic to install units at Halifax, the port where almost all North Atlantic convoys were mustered and from whence they sailed, often into the wolf packs of German submarines waiting patiently outside the Halifax harbor.

At Halifax radar would serve a twofold purpose. At night it would scan for enemy submarines, which often surfaced outside the port and charged their batteries under cloak of darkness. And it would also be used to guide the convoys out to sea in darkness or under cover of the dense fogs which often blanketed the harbor.

Birtchell arrived at the Halifax Naval Headquarters full of enthusiasm for his new assignment and was ushered into the presence of the admiral in charge of the port. While the young commander stood at ramrod attention, the old admiral slowly placed two sheets of writing paper on his desk and inserted a letter opener between the two sheets. Then he spoke:

"That's how much room we have for the likes of you around here. Get out!"

As any sailor knows, you can't argue with an admiral when you're only a commander, and it took the intervention of the Canadian Minister of National Defense to install this young officer in his new duties and put his radar gadgets into operation for the first time on the North American continent.

If the scientific and technical development of radar was accelerated by the war, it was the superbly engineered production system of the United States that gave radar its prominence and put it into common and relatively inexpensive use. More than 200 manufacturers and some 2,000 subcontractors participated in this postwar scientific achievement.

One of the first, and certainly one of the most important, uses of radar was the establishment of the Ground Control Approach system (GCA) at airports along both sides of the North Atlantic to guide airliners to safe landings after long ocean crossings when their fuel was low and airports were immobilized by fog and other bad weather. It was a godsend on countless occasions.

Yet, most pilots did not trust GCA. They preferred to depend on their own sensing devices rather than on pulses of radio frequency. Not a few of them died because of this mistrust of radar. Of course, there were instances in which an airliner came to roost on an airport terminal lawn rather than on a concrete runway, but these incidents were few and far between, and can be attributed to the birth pains of radar know-how. One pilot curtly dismissed a GCA request at Prestwick in 1948 and collided with the only hill north of the airport, killing everyone aboard his *Constellation* including himself.

GCA today is so perfected that ground controllers can guide an aircraft within tolerances as close as one foot too high or low over glide paths to airport runways at all our major cities.

This is Ground Control Approach in operation with a T-33 jet approaching for a landing. GCA of this type is portable and able to move at a moment's notice. (Raytheon photo)

In this application of radar, two interlocking systems are used. One scanner picks up the aircraft some thirty miles away and directs it to a compass heading which will line it up with the active runway. The other scanner superimposes the blip of the aircraft on a scope on which is inlaid a graduated glide path leading to the very threshold of the active runway. In this manner, the plane can be "talked down" by a controller watching its progress along the glide path. It is actually possible for the controller to provide the pilot with height and heading, speed and altitude, right to the point where the wheels make contact with the concrete of the runway.

As an example of how GCA operates, let's simulate a landing procedure at Prestwick Airport, located in Ayrshire on the southeastern coast of Scotland. A transatlantic flight begins its descent from 34,000 feet over Ireland to a height of 6,000 feet just west of the Isle of Ailsa Craig, and now the pilot calls Prestwick Tower. He is informed that the field conditions are bad, with fog and rain, and visibility not more than half a mile and the ceiling down to less than 200 feet. After weighing the situation, the pilot radios Prestwick and requests GCA in this manner:

"Ah, Prestwick . . . this is Flight Six-oh-four at six thousand estimating Prestwick at 1620 hours and requesting a GCA, please. Our present heading is zero eight zero, and our air speed is 270 knots. . . . Over."

"Ah, Roger, Six-oh-four, this is Prestwick GCA. We have you in range nicely and suggest you make a right turn now to zero nine zero and hold at six thousand. Are you getting any ice?"

"Six-oh-four . . . Roger at zero nine zero. Ah, no ice . . . but heavy cloud and rain patches. Over."

"Flight Six-oh-four, descend to two thousand feet at 500 per minute and make a left turn to heading zero two zero."

"Roger, two thousand and zero two zero and we're reducing to 200 knots."

"Okay, Six-oh-four, you're making your turn right on the button and your heading is good and now reduce to 160 knots and give her fifteen degrees of flap."

"Roger, GCA."

"Ah, Flight Six-oh-four, this is Prestwick GCA. Do you read clear?"

"Loud and clear."

"You are now ten miles out, your heading is nice, and now reduce altitude to one thousand feet and report."

"Roger, GCA, to one thousand on zero two zero."

"Six-oh-four, your air speed has climbed slightly, reduce to 160 knots. You're five miles out and a little to the left . . . turn right slightly . . . that's enough and straighten her out on zero two zero . . . very nice. You're four miles out and heading is good . . . three miles out and reduce to five hundred feet."

"Roger, five hundred feet, zero two zero . . . ah . . . ah . . . we're at five hundred now and leveling. . . ."

"You're forty feet too high . . . Six-oh-four. Now thirty feet too high . . . easy. You're ten feet too low . . . up now and easy . . . steady. You're five feet too high . . . steady. You're one mile out and your heading is good. Reduce power to 140 knots . . . descend to four hundred . . . three hundred . . . two hundred . . . hold. You're five feet too low . . . two feet too high . . . full flaps now . . . keep your air speed to 135 knots. One foot too high . . . steady. You should be over the high intensity flares . . . your heading of zero two zero is good. You should see the runway threshold any second . . . ease her to one hundred feet . . . to fifty feet . . . very nice. You're two feet too high . . . very nice. . . ."

"Ah, Prestwick, I see the runway, I'm pulling off power. My God it's foggy. We're on the ground . . . now where the hell is the airport?"

"Nice landing, Six-oh-four. We're sending a car to guide you in . . . continue to the second intersection on your right, and now Ground will take over. So long."

"Roger . . . and thanks, GCA."

Ground Controlled Approach is only one of the many fine applications of radar to present-day commercial flying. The most important application of all is the combination radar installation on the ground and in the cockpit which scans the weather and assists the trained analyst to forecast accurately the coming events on the flight path.

In the field of weather forecasting by advanced radar, the United States is, at the moment, second to none.

It was on August 1, 1956, that the United States Weather Bureau made a belated move to improve its forecasting of dangerous storms. What was sorely needed in this country was earlier and more reliable storm warnings, and, armed with four million dollars, the Bureau signed a contract with Raytheon, one of the nation's top electronic concerns, located in Waltham, Mass., for thirty-nine advanced radar units, eight of which were to be set up by the United States Navy's Bureau of Aeronautics.

By strategic placing of these new long-range radars, the Weather Bureau hoped to tie together a chain of loosely knit reporting units into a network that could watch the skies over the country and report the movement of weather forces in a split second to any part of the nation at any time of the day. With all the sets installed, weather changes could be instantly pinpointed and updated from minute to minute. Communities would, therefore, be warned in plenty of time of approaching severe weather, including hurricanes, tornadoes, and other damaging wind forces. Airliners would be kept advised of dangerous storms along their routes.

It all seemed too good to be true.

The Raytheon units would be able to identify storms as far away as 250 miles and to scan 200,000 square miles of sky. At Miami, where weather forecasting has always been an intense struggle because of the frequency of dangerous storms, experts were looking forward to the arrival of the new units, whose precision would soon make it possible for them to predict an hour in advance the exact minute when rain would begin to fall on any street or beach within 100 miles of the Weather Bureau's office.

Rotating both horizontally and vertically to reveal atmos-

Recently installed at Miami's International Airport is this giant radar, known to the trade as a Weather Service Radar-57, produced and developed by the Raytheon Company for the U. S. Weather Bureau. (Raytheon photo)

pheric cross sections, the new sets would be hooked up to movie cameras so that precipitation areas could be recorded for later research studies and for aircraft accident investigation, although, with such modern radar equipment about, no one seriously thought that aircraft would blunder into dangerous storms.

The first of these new panoramic probers was delivered to the Weather Bureau on June 1, 1959, and in quick succession others followed and were soon installed in key locations across the country. Now it was possible for trained radar operators to plot not only the storm's depth and frontal edge but also, by magnifying their echoes, to single out the particular sections of extreme danger. The shape and exact location of each storm's trouble spot could now be enlarged and plotted with infinite care and attention.

Sets were installed in Washington, D. C., Apalachicola, Fla., Kansas City, Mo., Columbia, Mo., Wilmington, N. C., Evansville, Ind., Sacramento, Calif., Brownsville, Texas, Daytona Beach, Fla., Oklahoma City, Okla., Charleston, S. C., Des Moines, Iowa, Key West, Fla., Wichita, Kansas, Cincinnati, Ohio, and St. Louis, Mo.

As can be seen, the radar units were strategically placed to track vast frontal systems from coast to coast and to concentrate on the dangerous "tornado alleys" of the Midwest and the tropical storm-spawning areas of the Gulf and the Caribbean.

While all this was going on, the U. S. Army received an advanced combat radar unit, mounted on a trailer, which would monitor the movement of clouds resulting from nuclear bursts as well as track storms 400 miles away. Operated by the Army Signal Corps, the new unit featured a powerful antenna that moved up from the sliding roof of the mobile van to sweep the skies with twice the detection capability of the earlier models first introduced to the Signal Corps in 1946.

However, the idea of updating weather forecasting by the use of advanced radar was not confined to the United States alone. The trend was becoming world wide.

The Swedish Government purchased fourteen units similar to those ordered by the U. S. Weather Bureau. Manufactured in Italy under licensing from Raytheon, the sets were divided between permanent and mobile locations, providing the Swedish Weather Bureau and military forces with a forecasting system unparalleled in Northern Europe. Special sensitivity was built into these sets so that small weather balloons, equipped with radar reflectors, could be spotted and tracked as far as 100 miles from the units, augmenting the normal 125,000-square-mile detection sweep of the sets.

On the other side of the globe, the Australian Bureau of Meteorology installed something novel in radar detection. One of several new units, attached to a tremendous antenna, was installed atop Saddle Mountain in Queensland, far up the Australian coast. The object of this remote installation was to track tropical storms spawned as far distant as the Coral Sea, which on many occasions would sweep unannounced into Australian waters and across the mainland with tremendous fury, resulting in high losses of life, livestock, and crops. This radar unit was hooked up to a microwave system (similar to the system used in the United States to transmit television sound and pictures across the country) and beamed to the cities on the southeast coast. Its giant dish antenna, 2,000 feet above the surrounding seas, could give ample warning of cyclones hours and even days away from the mainland.

Elsewhere around the world similar installations were either in the planning stage or being installed. Coupled with information from the Telstar satellite, they could track vast intercontinental and world-wide storm movements for the benefit of all nations.

Augmenting the domestic system of weather radar surveillance were the units in modern civilian and military passenger airliners and transports. Much smaller in scope, their principal use was to help the pilots avoid turbulence, hail, and other severe weather formations along the flight path. However, these sets had limitations. They could only detect turbulence associated with the phenomenon of shear.

It is a breath-taking sight to behold the frothy black turbulence of a thunderstorm beneath the wings of an aircraft. Cloud currents, whipped by violent updrafts, can be seen between the towers of the upward-moving castles of cumulus, boiling with energy that dwarfs the atomic bomb. (Photo by Martin Caidin)

As mentioned earlier, turbulence is caused by shear, and shear occurs when the wind varies in its direction and its speed. The degree of this turbulence is directly proportional to the difference in the speed of the wind, the flow direction, or both.

Turbulence is extreme in thunderstorms because the vertical currents of air are flowing in opposite directions at very high rates of speed. These are the updrafts and the rain-laden downdrafts.

The degree of turbulence encountered by an airplane flying through such an area of shear is dependent upon two things— how fast the aircraft passes through the shear zone and how sharply defined the shear zone is. To a certain extent, the pilot has some control over the degree of turbulence he flies into, because he can often perceive the shear line and slow down the speed of his aircraft for the penetration period. All airliners are equipped with manuals which outline the penetration speed into such turbulent areas. However, the speed of a modern jet often carries it into a shear before there is time to slow down or take evasive action, and then, as happened recently in a Boeing 707 of Eastern Air Lines flying from Tampa to Dallas, every passenger in the aircraft may have his dinner slopped over him.

Radar, therefore, should be used by the pilot to pick out a flight path through a gradual shear area where the lines between the updrafts and downdrafts are not so pronounced. Of course, the wisest policy is to avoid the area entirely by making a detour around it.

Since almost all airliner radar sets are of the contour circuitry type, sometimes referred to as iso-echo, the pilot can "see" the shear and avoid the areas of maximum turbulence. The distinct and dangerous pictures of shear appear on the radarscope like circles or oblongs of light. Pilots call them "cheerios" because they look like the breakfast cereal of that name.

The contouring circuitry blanks out some of the return echoes above a fixed degree of brightness and the echoes of the storm appear on the scope with considerable difference in intensity. One storm may look like a thick doughnut. It has not returned an echo of sharp shear and to fly through it would provide this pattern: smooth, light rain and very little turbulence, moderate rain and light turbulence, heavy rain and light turbulence, moderate rain, light rain, and out. However, the thin type of return, a very thin cheerio with sharply defined lines, should be avoided. The most severe turbulence is always pictured as this thin circle of light. In fact, pilots should be suspicious of any echoes that have well-defined edges.

Some airliners do not have radar sets of the contour circuitry type, but by the manipulation of the gain control of the standard radar, only the intense precipitation areas will come through. The elimination of weak echoes will often unmask the tiny fingers, indicating hail fingers or tornadoes, that poke from the cloud edges. Pointing fingers, hooked fingers or scalloped edges mean danger.

Some storms change their shape rapidly, and hail shafts will appear so quickly that a pilot must be on his toes to notice the change. While battling turbulence, it is sometimes impossible for the pilot to fly and maintain adequate radar surveillance at the same time. Perhaps it might be a good suggestion to have radar technicians on all jet airliners as an added safety factor.

The Directorate of Flight Safety for the RCAF Headquarters in Ottawa, Canada, suggests in a recent publication: Don't use radar to find out why it's rough . . . use it to avoid areas which may be rough.

Several suggestions, among many, to pilots using radar and flying near dangerous-looking cloud formations are given here:

—Be sure and tilt the antenna to see the region you are about to fly through.

—Avoid "figure six" echoes. (This is cheerio with a hail finger.)

—Fly at least five miles from storms below freezing level and at least ten miles from storms above freezing level.

—Avoid by at least ten miles any storm which is changing shape rapidly.

—Monitor the scope constantly when in storm areas.

—Fly clear of rapidly developing storm echoes.

—Never fly under an overhang of a thunderstorm cloud. If you do, you are asking to be struck by hail.

—Be interested in any target beyond forty or fifty miles which appears on the scope.

The RCAF and the MATS flyers, from which some of these suggestions are reprinted, show the terrific interest taken in the subject by the safety directors. But, as the old saying goes, you can lead a horse to water but you can't make him drink.

Often airline pilots have turned off their radar sets because they didn't believe, from the appearance of cloud formations, that there was any turbulence ahead. Yet it's an established fact that in the hands of a trained operator radar can guide the pilot along a smooth avenue as long as he searches out storm areas at least thirty to fifty miles ahead, so as not to be trapped in a blind alley by storms building up rapidly on either side of his flight path. Flying into a blind alley can be most uncomfortable and dangerous for crew and passengers. Some pilots admit that when they become trapped in turbulence, it is often impossible to watch the radar and fly at the same time. It then becomes necessary for the pilot or co-pilot to scan the unit and call out the signals as is done by the Hurricane Hunters when they fly into the jaws of cyclones—the radar operator calling the areas of smoothness to the pilots.

If the foregoing makes radar seem infallible, there are two sides to every question. There are many pilots who are of the opinion that many present-day radar installations are not doing the job.

A captain of a transatlantic DC-8 jet said recently that often his radar does not disclose thunderstorm cells, particularly if there is a considerable number of thick clouds in the air.

"On one of my flights, I saw ahead of me and slightly to the right a giant thundercloud. I was climbing up to the assigned level of 33,000 feet and I scanned this cloud with my radar. I could see no cell, no shear lines at all. Yet it was obviously a thunderhead and the lightning was playing all through it. I flew alongside of it and directed my radar into the cloud and

Lockheed Super Constellations *of this type, with long-range turbo-compound engines, are crammed with radar equipment to detect and plot the movement of tropical storms that might endanger life and property. The same aircraft is vital to radar coverage off both coasts for the North America Air Defense Command.* (U. S. Air Force photo)

still did not get a shear line return. A pilot not seeing such a build-up could fly right into it without knowing it.

"Some sets are good. Others are only fair. I have seen installations in some planes that just weren't worth their salt. Others gave good returns. On the North Atlantic we don't need our radar very much, but we always turn it on when our navigator tells us we're one hundred miles from the Irish coast. Seeing the outline of land in the set is always reassuring, and it gives us the chance to check on our navigator's work."

Trans-Canada Air Lines has come up with a new idea. A radar technician is now flying on flights when thunderstorms are predicted along the route, just to check the operation of the radar under these routine storm conditions. His report may have a far-reaching effect on all flight operations in thunderstorm areas.

Airborne investigations of this kind, coupled with reports of airline safety councils and on-hand evidence from the pilots themselves, may yet come up with a fool-proof system of detecting trouble in the crowded, cloud-filled skies. It most certainly will lead to improvements in radar detection.

Death in the Everglades 10

ONE WOULD HAVE THOUGHT that the lessons of the past aug-
mented by the world's finest weather surveillance systems on
the ground and in hundreds of airliners in every corner of the
globe, supported by the ever-watchful Telstar, would have
made the year 1963 relatively free of storm disasters. But not so.

The year of 1963 will go down in aviation history as the worst
storm disaster period in the annals of commercial aviation.
More than 300 persons lost their lives and some two score were
injured as seven airliners were lost and two others sustained
near-misses by performing terrifying acrobatics in turbulent
skies. Several transports received damaging lightning strikes.

Things got off to a bad start on February 11 when some of
the worst winter weather on record struck the North American
continent. A large Arctic high-pressure system worked southward and eastward over the bitter Canadian plains into the
western part of South Dakota. Its chilly blasts extended from
the mid-Rockies to the Appalachians and as far south as the
Gulf of Mexico, embracing both sides of the Gulf from Yucatan
to the Florida Keys. Within this broad expanse, temperatures
dropped below freezing and hundreds of communities suffered
the coldest winter on record. A cold front encircled this vast
high-pressure area, creating long bands of precipitation.

Snow fell in Texas, Louisiana, Mississippi, Colorado, Oklahoma, Utah, and parts of Arizona. More than a foot of snow fell in the highlands of New Mexico. Snow covered the Appalachians and everything north and west of them. However, as the cold front moved eastward and southward into the warming range of the Atlantic Plain and the Gulf states, this snow turned into rain, and severe thunderstorms and dangerous tornadoes churned their leisurely way along the leading edge of the frontal zone.

Behind this violence came more snow. Places like South Carolina, Georgia, and central Florida experienced violent tropical rains and thunderstorms one moment and snow the next. Millions of dollars in crops and citrus fruits were destroyed as icy fingers reached into these subtropical areas. Many of the showers which preceded the cold front were laced with hail to compound the damage to fruit and vegetable crops. Along with this, the entire Atlantic seaboard was cloaked in fog and rain.

By the next day, February 12, the cold front had moved steadily eastward and southward, and by 1 P.M., Eastern standard time, had formed a line that stretched from below the Yucatan Peninsula northeastward to the extreme southern part of Florida and out to sea. Along this line, dense cumulus cloud banks filled the skies as the dominating cold mass of air forced the warm moist air upward into the great heights of the thinning atmosphere. And, as is typical of an intrusion of this kind, thunderstorms with their squall lines, damaging winds, hail and torrential rains lashed Florida with black and frothy fury. Ugly twisters dipped and swirled across the south-central part of Florida. The day turned dark. An unprecedented six inches of rain fell in Hillsborough County, three inches on Tampa, almost five inches at Pompano and Vero Beach, and so on around the state.

Isolated thunderstorms formed tremendous cloud castles which blotted out the sun. Huge anvils, looking like giant mushrooms, moved through the skies, but because of the thick swirling squalls below they were invisible from the ground or, for that matter, from anywhere below 30,000 feet.

All this bad weather was predictable weather. It was as typical of a cold front as those described in every pilot's textbook. And, in fact, it had been predicted with good accuracy by the weathermen. But, in southern Florida, one didn't have to be a forecaster to see that dangerously bad weather was on the march. High winds and rain, embellished with rolling scud clouds and high gusts, moved ponderously from the Gulf to the Atlantic, and Florida was caught in between.

What could anyone accomplish on a day such as this was the question asked by thousands upon thousands of Florida vacationers. Their holidays this winter had been continuously plagued by cold and rain, and many of them either headed for the Caribbean islands or just became fed up and went home.

However, three Northern couples thought they had the best answer for a day such as this. They would go fishing into the wildest area of the Florida Everglades, marked on the map as the Everglades National Park. Vacationing at Naples, on the southwest coast, the three couples started down the coast to the lonely hamlet of Flamingo, and despite the fog and drizzle and the ominous rumbling of distant thunder they agreed to push on into the swamps, in the age-old belief that rainy weather is good fishing weather.

At ten o'clock, Gordon Schwan, a Mansfield, Ohio, businessman, and leader of the group, gripped the wheel of his cabin cruiser and inched his way out of the Flamingo Ranger Station dock. With him was his wife Marilou, and two other couples, Mr. and Mrs. Conrad Schardt, of Cleveland, and Mr. and Mrs. John Mortorff, of Indianapolis.

Schwan took the cruiser across the choppy waters of Whitewater Bay to the entrance of the Shark River. Then he steered into the jungle of river systems in this tropical wilderness known as the Banana Patch. He knew the way. He had fished there several times before.

It was 11 A.M.

Some fifty-eight miles northeast of this lonely fishing spot, Hubbard Davis arrived by automobile at Miami's International

Airport, intending to fly to Palm Beach sixty-five miles north of Miami and spend the day with friends. He went to the hangar on the north side of the airport where his twin-engined Piper *Apache* was kept. After arranging to have the aircraft checked out by his mechanic, he went to the phone and called the weather forecaster.

"How's my weather up to Palm Beach?" he asked.

"Pretty bad," replied the forecaster. "There's a squall line moving into the vicinity and we expect wind gusts up to forty-five miles an hour with heavy rain and the chance of some severe weather."

"Um-m-m, that's not so good."

"If you don't have to fly this morning, I would advise you to stay on the ground," said the forecaster, and Davis agreed with him. He turned to the mechanic and told him to wheel the Piper back into its berth. The weather just wasn't fit for flying, he had decided.

At the same moment this incident was taking place, the airport weather forecaster was posting a warning that pilots could expect isolated severe thunderstorms, numerous heavy showers, moderate to severe turbulence, and the chance of hail aloft for some time.

Elsewhere in Miami, at this time of the morning, these other interesting events were taking place:

—A lawyer filed suit in circuit court against Northwest Airlines for a widow, Mrs. Frieda Graboski, whose husband had been killed in a crash eighteen months before.

—Residents of Miami had just received their issue of the Miami *Herald* and were chuckling over the story that transatlantic stewardesses were reporting from London, England, that they were suffering from an occupational disease which they called "jet-age tummy."

The girls reported that some of their number were "swelling up like balloons," and a few had been forced to slip into the galley behind closed curtains and remove their girdles rather than bear this jet-age pain.

London doctors, always ready to comment on such ticklish situations, warned all stewardesses everywhere that if they wore tight girdles they would swell up even more—as gases in the tummy at such heights would expand as much as 90 per cent. It was an unusual situation, to say the least.

Fortunately, domestic stewardesses were not experiencing "jet-age tummy" on their flights, probably because the flights were of reasonably short duration.

Shortly after noon on this February 12, five such domestic stewardesses checked in with Northwest Orient Airlines operations office, at Miami's International Airport. They were assigned to Flight 705, a nonstop service from Miami to Chicago. Despite the bad weather, the flight was scheduled to operate at its regular time, departing from Miami at 1:30 P.M.

A few of the passengers, anxious to get the choicest seats on the Chicago-bound jet, had already arrived and had begun checking in at the Northwest counter in the center of this busy terminal. One young blonde traveler was pacing up and down, uncertain as to what to do. The weather was so bad that she was reluctant to fly. When she had convinced herself that the risk wasn't worth while, she marched up to the Northwest counter and canceled her reservation. She was the smartest person in Miami's International Airport that black Tuesday. It was unfortunate that the thirty-five other passengers at the airport that day did not feel the same way.

Elsewhere at the Miami airport the ground crew of Northwest Airlines was servicing the Boeing 720B jet airliner which would soon shuttle those five stewardesses and a one-third capacity load of impatient air travelers to Chicago. Departure time was only half an hour away.

The 720B which was being refueled and checked out was a sister ship of the famous 707 but slightly smaller in size. Rivulets of rain water coursed off her 2,433 square feet of wing area. She was 136 feet 2 inches in length, more than 41 feet high, and boasted a wing span of 130 feet 10 inches.

A Northwest Airlines 720B fan jet is shown here in flight in heavy cloud. (Northwest Orient Airline photo)

And what a plane she was, able to cruise at close to 615 miles an hour for 3,600 miles with a gross weight of an almost incredible 216,000 pounds. Her service ceiling was 41,000 feet, and her four Pratt & Whitney turbo-fan engines could each account for 18,000 pounds of thrust. She had 41 per cent more power than her immediate predecessors, the 720's without the fan jets. The plane had first flown on October 6, 1960, and since then had chalked up an excellent record of reliability.

The 720B was nine feet shorter than the 707 and her maximum take-off weight was less by 13,000 pounds. Still she had a lot of scamper, and with her weight-to-power ratio was one of the fastest airliners in the world. And on this squally Tuesday, her commander would be a handsome forty-seven-year-old Minneapolis bachelor, Roy W. Almquist.

Captain Almquist had started flying with Northwest on July 12, 1942. He was a man of extensive interests. He was president of a bank at Savage, Minnesota, part owner of a Ford dealership in Rosemount, Minnesota, and president of the Rosemount City school bus company. He was a director of Dyna-Mation, Inc., a research and development firm for precision machine tools. On top of all this, he was president of the Rosemount Lions Club.

But today Roy Almquist, a competent, sincere, dedicated pilot, was concerned with only one thing: flying Northwest Orient's hot Flight 705 to Chicago—705 being the number of this particular flight and not the type of airplane. Being the conscientious pilot that he was, Capt. Almquist was deeply concerned about the worsening weather. At 1 P.M. he carefully read the latest Weather Bureau bulletin. It reported an approaching squall line with cumulo-nimbus (thunderheads) rising up to 30,000 feet. He talked with the airway's forecasters and then chatted with his crew about the weather.

It would be his decision whether to fly or not to fly. It is almost always the pilot's decision to make, because once the pilot is at the controls he is the man in charge of the aircraft as well as the safety and security of the passengers in all but the most unusual circumstances.

Boeing 707's, such as the sleek airliner shown here over coastal cumulous cloud formations, have tangled with thunderstorms, which show no favorites. (Photo courtesy Air France)

Roy Almquist decided to fly. Perhaps he thought he had the solution to get around the obviously severe weather astride his path to the west of Miami. In any event his mind seemed to be made up. Almquist's judgments had always been good judgments. His fellow pilots knew him as a pilot who was cautious to the extreme. "If things weren't perfect," one of his friends said, "Roy just wouldn't go."

Captain Almquist's decision to operate Flight 705 was the go-ahead signal for Northwest Orient agents to board the passengers. There would be thirty-five of them for this "Regal Imperial," for that's what the flight was called. There would have been thirty-six passengers but for the pretty blonde in the beige suit who had canceled because she didn't like flying in rainy weather. But the others were ready to go—twenty men, including an Indianapolis millionaire; twelve women; two girls, both fifteen; and an eighteen-year-old boy, eager for the thrill of jet flying.

The announcement of the flight sent the passengers scurrying along Concourse 2 to the departure gate, where the magnificent five-million-dollar jet lay quiet and docile on the tarmack, ready for the short hop to Chicago. There would be no sweat on this flight. The plane would be only one-third loaded.

Meanwhile, the eight crew members had gone on board and were busy at their assigned duties. Captain Almquist was seated at the left side of the flight deck, his starched white shirt and black tie contrasting with the dim interior and the many diminutive colored lights of the massive instrument panel. His only view at this moment was straight ahead through the windshield. In his sight was the window of the Concourse and peering through it were a number of curious visitors, gawking at the tremendous front of the 720B jet only inches from their noses.

At Almquist's right sat First Officer Robert J. Feller, thirty-eight-year-old Rochester, Minnesota-born father of a son and daughter. A veteran flier, he had joined Northwest back in October 1946, and had resided since that time in Minneapolis, the home base of the airline.

At the intricate engineering panel of the giant jet, to the rear of Feller, sat Second Officer Allen R. Friesen, twenty-nine, of Hopkins, Minnesota. Born in Rock Springs, Wyoming, he had graduated from high school in Middleton, Idaho, married, and then joined Northwest on April 4, 1949. He and his wife had adopted a baby Korean girl who was now two years old and the idol of her father's eyes. Before joining the airline, Friesen had worked for Boeing and knew Boeing's jets like a book.

This was a plush flight, this Flight 705, with five pretty stewardesses ready to receive and take care of only thirty-five passengers. One of the stewardesses was blonde Wendy Engebretson, twenty-two, the daughter of Mr. and Mrs. E. Forsythe Engebretson, of Bismarck, North Dakota. Her dad was a well-known attorney. Her uncle Max Miller had died on March 17, 1960, when a Northwest Airlines *Electra* had come apart in the air and crashed at Tell City, Indiana. Wendy had graduated from Bismarck High School and attended Mills College in Oakland, California. The violent death of her uncle did not deter her from her ambition to be a stewardess and she had no regrets in her choice of a career.

Myrna Ewert was the oldest of the five girls. She was twenty-eight, and a native of Michell, South Dakota. She had attended high school in Bensenville, Illinois, and colleges in Minneapolis and St. Paul before joining Northwest.

Virginia Lee Younkin, twenty-five, was a gay, vivacious stewardess, always grinning, who loved life and loved flying. She was a tall, good-natured Texan, having been born in Dallas, but she had graduated from Monrovia-Duarte High School in Monrovia, California, before traveling to Minneapolis to join Northwest.

Connie Rae Blank had the big grin that ideally suited her rounded face and she enjoyed chatting with the passengers at every possible opportunity. She was just twenty-one and was born in Spokane, Washington, where she had graduated from Lewis and Clark High School before attending Washington State College at Pullman, Washington. She had joined Northwest on April 28, 1962.

Mary Sandell was the newest addition to the group. She was twenty—the baby—and had only recently joined Northwest, two days before the Christmas of 1962. Minneapolis-born and a graduate of Washburn High in that city, she had gone to college briefly at Nevada, Missouri, before becoming an airline stewardess.

It was exactly 1:15 P.M.

Rain fell in black curtains across the airport. The skies were so dark the passengers thought they were looking out on a late evening scene of the normal northern winter from which they had spent so much to escape. It became so dark, in fact, that street lights automatically came on. Gale winds lashed the airport, shaking even the giant jets at their moorings. It was a bad day, and no doubt about it.

At 1:23 P.M., Captain Almquist adjusted his earphones, put his microphone to his lips and called Ground Control at the Miami Airport Tower:

"Ah, Ground, Northwest Seven-oh-five . . . we're about to start engines. Ah, how are they vectoring out? We're going IFR to Chicago . . . any chance for a radar vector around some of this?"

"Yes, sir, they're doing the best they can. It's a pretty—ah—thick line . . . northwest of us. Most of the . . . ah . . . either through a southwest climb or a southeast climb, and then back over the top of it . . . what most people are doing."

"O.K. That's what we kinda planned on . . . wondered if it was the same thing yet."

"All right, sir . . . ah . . . give me a call under power."

"O.K."

The flight had now backed away from the Miami terminal and was lumbering under power toward the distant take-off runways. The roar of jets coming and going was drowned out by its own jets taking on extra power for the quick trip to the outer perimeter of the airfield.

The flight now called Ground Control of Miami, the section concerned with the movement of the aircraft while it was on airport property.

Northwest. Miami Ground Control. Northwest Seven-oh-five is now under way . . . IFR Chicago. Go ahead.

[*Captain Almquist was informing the Tower he would fly to Chicago under Instrument Flight Rules—on a controlled airway all the way, and he wanted to know his runway for take-off.*]

Tower. Northwest Seven-zero-five . . . Roger. Runway Three-zero . . . hold short of [Runway] Two-seven left. Wind two nine zero degrees at two five.

[*The Tower was telling Almquist that his take-off runway was 27 left. This meant he would take off on a heading of 270 degrees, into the 25-mile-an-hour wind blowing from the northwest.*]

Northwest. O.K.

Tower. Northwest S-s-seven-zero-five, a twin Cessna holding on the run-up pad, use caution . . . contact Clearance Delivery . . . one two seven point five for your clearance.

Northwest. Ah . . . one two seven five . . . Roger.

[*Captain Almquist and his flight crew switched radio frequencies at this point to Tower Clearance Delivery (CD).*]

Northwest. Northwest Seven-oh-five . . . on clearance.

Tower. Northwest Seven-zero-five . . . ah . . . didn't channel . . . try it again.

Northwest. Northwest Seven-oh-five on clearance.

Tower. Northwest Seven-oh-five. How do you read?

[*Tower Clearance Delivery wants to know if the flight can hear it clearly and intelligibly, but there is no answer at the moment as another activity cuts in.*]

Tower. Twin Cessna two hundred zee . . . stand by. Northwest Seven-oh-five, Miami Ground Control, do you read?

Northwest. Yeah, you're loud and clear now. Go ahead.

Tower. Northwest Seven-zero-five's cleared to the Chicago O'Hare Airport, via Jay Forty-one radials, Saint Petersburg, flight plan route, maintain three thousand. Expect further clearance at flight level two five zero, ten minutes after Cypress Intersection. After take-off, turn right, heading three six zero for vector to Jay Forty-one radials.

[*The controller had now given Almquist his route for a few minutes after the take-off. He was to make a right-hand turn into the north while other aircraft had been turning to the southeast or to the southwest. There is little doubt that Almquist didn't like this, as will be seen in a moment, but he repeated the message according to the rules.*]

NORTHWEST. Northwest Seven-oh-five is cleared to Chicago O'Hare via the radials of Jay Forty-one vector, Saint Pete, flight plan route, maintain three thousand. Expect flight level two five zero, radar vector to the Vortac. Northwest Seven-oh-five changing Tower.

[*The flight was about to change its radio frequency to the Tower Local Control for the actual take-off, and the flight would now be under the vigilance of the controllers in the Miami Tower, high above the airport terminal, above the administration levels, the hotel and restaurants.*]

TOWER. Northwest Seven-oh-five, clearance correct . . . Tower . . . one one eight three.

NORTHWEST. Miami Tower . . . Northwest Seven-oh-five is ready.

TOWER (*now under the local controller*). Northwest Seven-zero-five, taxi into position, [Runway] Two-seven left and hold.

NORTHWEST. O.K. Two seven left . . . and—ah—they gave us a right turn to three six zero. We would kinda like to take that southeast vector, if they'll give it to us.

[*Almquist wanted no part of the storm area. It seemed to be his opinion that a right-hand turn after his take-off would put him right into the teeth of the trouble. Other planes were going southwest and southeast after take-off, and he thought that southeast would be by far the safest, taking off and turning away from the storm, gaining height all the while and then flying over it to St. Petersburg and onward to Chicago. Almquist would not have asked for this routing unless he thought it was the safest at the moment. He was using good common sense.*]

TOWER. Stand by.

NORTHWEST. Er—Tower, this is Northwest Seven . . . [*unintelligible*]

TOWER. . . . moment ago, we're co-ordinating now to see what we can get. Hold in position, [Runway] Two-seven left.

NORTHWEST. O.K. We'd just as soon hold rather than make a right turn out.

TOWER. O.K. We got a left turn now, heading one eight zero for a vector out.

NORTHWEST. That's real fine.

TOWER. O.K. Taxi into position and hold. I'll have departure clearance in a few seconds.

NORTHWEST. O.K.

TOWER. Northwest Seven-zero-five is cleared for take-off, [Runway] Two-seven left.

NORTHWEST. Seven-oh-five . . . Roger.

TOWER. Northwest Seven-zero-five, contact Departure Control, one one nine seven.

NORTHWEST. One nineteen seven . . . Roger.

NORTHWEST. And Northwest—ah—Seven—ah—oh-five on departure.

[At this second, the huge 720B was roaring down the runway into the 25-knot northwest wind.]

TOWER (*now it's Departure Control calling the messages*). So long, Northwest Seven-zero-five, Miami Departure Control radar contact. Continue the left turn, heading of one two zero, maintain three thousand. This will be a vector around the precipitation area.

[Departure Control was telling the Northwest flight to continue making its left turn, now that it was off the ground, to the required heading, and to keep at the altitude of 3,000 feet until told to do otherwise. According to the radar control at Miami, this routing would take the flight around the heavy precipitation which could be seen in the radarscopes, and precipitation meant turbulence.]

NORTHWEST. O.K. Left to one two zero, maintain three. Northwest Seven-oh-five.

TOWER. Roger.

TOWER. Northwest Seven-zero-five, turn right now, to a heading of one eight zero.

NORTHWEST. O.K. Back right to one eight zero. Seven-oh-five.

TOWER. Roger.

NORTHWEST. Northwest Seven-oh-five maintaining three.

TOWER. Northwest Seven-zero-five, Roger.

TOWER. What is your present heading, Northwest Seven-oh-five?

NORTHWEST. One eight zero. Seven-oh-five.

TOWER. Roger, Northwest Seven-oh-five—ah-h—climb and maintain five thousand now.

NORTHWEST. O.K. Out of three for five.

TOWER. Northwest Seven-zero-five, continue the right turn of a heading of—ah—two four zero.

NORTHWEST. O.K. Right to two four zero. Seven-oh-five.

TOWER. Northwest Seven-Oh-five, maintain four thousand.

NORTHWEST. Seven-oh-five . . . we're at and will maintain four.

TOWER. What is your altitude now?

NORTHWEST. We're at four thousand.

TOWER. Mighty fine, maintain four thousand . . . continue heading to one eight zero.

NORTHWEST. O.K. Turning back to one eight zero. Seven-oh-five.

[*Departure Control was changing the flight's routing in order to vector it into the path of least precipitation and the zigzagging continued.*]

TOWER. Northwest Seven-zero-five . . . turn right now, heading of two four zero.

NORTHWEST. Ah-h-h, right to two four zero. Seven-oh-five.

TOWER. Roger, Northwest Seven-zero-five, now you can climb to maintain five thousand.

NORTHWEST. O.K. Out of four for five. Seven-oh-five.

TOWER. Roger. Northwest Seven-zero-five, continue the right turn now, heading of two seven zero.

NORTHWEST. Right to two seven zero. Seven-oh-five.

TOWER. Northwest Seven-zero-five, continue the right turn now, heading three zero zero.

[*Flight 705 was being turned to a west-northwest direction over the Florida Everglades and southwest of Miami.*]

Northwest. Three zero zero, Roger . . . if we could go up now we'd be in good shape.

[*The flight has found a break in the storm which appears to be clear enough to climb through to cruising height, but permission must be granted to the flight, as other aircraft are flying in and out of Miami, and air corridors must be assigned each flight in relation to its destination and its position in the sky.*]

Tower. O.K. Stand by.

Northwest. Ah-h, Departure . . . Northwest Seven-oh-five— ah-h-h, it looks like we're going to run right back into this, at this altitude. Ah-h-h, is there a chance to go back southwest or east—ah-h-h—or climb?

[*The pilots of Flight 705 are reporting that the storm is in their path at their present altitude of 5,000 feet. It is a clear indication that the 720B's radar is performing and that the crew can see the heavy precipitation area as well as visually perceive the blackness on the flight path. Almquist and Feller want to get out of it.*]

Tower. Northwest Seven-zero-five, Roger. You'll enter a precipitation area in about four miles and you should be out in the clear for about three miles, then back into it again. However, north of the localizer and northwest of Jersey intersection you should break out in the clear and it should be okay from there on.

[*Departure Control is informing Almquist and Feller that the radar in Miami shows a belt of heavy rain just ahead of the flight, then a brief clear space, and then more rainfall. After that, the plane should break into the clear, after passing a radio checkpoint over the swamps.*]

Northwest. Ah-h-h, we're in the clear now. We can see it out ahead . . . looks pretty bad.

[*The flight can see the storm directly ahead and the pilot is concerned. He has already asked for a change in direction and this has not yet been granted to him, with the explanation that somewhere ahead in the next ten minutes clearer weather is waiting. But what is lying between is bothering Almquist, and the passengers by this time would be just as worried as he.*]

TOWER. O.K. Northwest Seven-zero-five . . . we're working on a higher altitude now.

NORTHWEST. O.K.

TOWER. Northwest Seven-zero-five, climb and maintain flight level two five zero and report leaving six and seven thousand.

[*The flight is now given permission to climb upward and report after leaving the 6,000- and 7,000-foot altitudes.*]

NORTHWEST. O.K. Ah-h-h . . . we'll make a left turn about thirty degrees here and climb out of five for two five zero now.

TOWER. All right, you want to turn to a heading of two seven zero, then?

NORTHWEST. That's okay and we'll go back out in the open again, then.

TOWER. Okay, Northwest Seven-zero-five.

NORTHWEST. O.K.

TOWER. And Northwest Seven-zero-five, what's your altitude now?

NORTHWEST. Ah-h-h . . . moderate to s-s—ah—to heavy turbulence . . . right through where you vectored us.

[*Almquist would have his automatic pilot turned off during all this time. He was into the blackness, and when he reported heavy turbulence, though he probably meant to say severe, he was being pounded unmercifully. Could his radar see the cell ahead?*]

TOWER. Northwest Seven-zero-five—ah, say again, what is your altitude?

NORTHWEST. We're out of nine now.

TOWER. Out of nine thousand, Roger. Can you—ah-h—turn right now?

NORTHWEST. Ah, negative . . . you vectored us right into that —ah—moderate to heavy turbulence . . . ah-h-h . . . we're out of ten now . . . we'll turn right as soon as we can.

[*This conversation from the flight shows that the turbulence is so severe it is impossible to make a turn to the right. Severe drafting during a turn can cause a high-speed jet to spin out of control and can slap it on its back in a split second. Almquist and Feller were not taking any chances of this happening.*]

Tower. Northwest Seven-zero-five . . . the vector I gave you was to the least—ah—turbulent area that I have indicated on the scope . . . stand by.

Northwest. O.K. You better run the rest of them off the other way then.

[*The flight is telling Miami Departure Control to route other airliners in directions other than the one which they gave to Flight 705. This route is so turbulent and so dangerous at this moment that Almquist and Feller are warning Control to keep others out of it. Should Almquist have turned back? Maybe he would have liked to do so, but the turbulence was so severe it was impossible to make the turn.*]

Tower. Northwest Seven-zero-five . . . your position's ten miles west of Rancho Intersection. You're out of ten thousand, I understand. Radar service terminated, contact the Center on one eighteen point nine.

[*This radio message means that Almquist was no longer under Departure radar control and was being advised to tune in the frequency of Miami Air Route Traffic Control Center.*]

Northwest. Ah, one eighteen nine, Roger. Miami Departure, Northwest Seven-oh-five . . . we're unable one eighteen nine.

[*The flight is unable to reach Air Traffic Control, probably because of severe static from the thunderstorms around the area.*]

Tower. Northwest Seven-zero-five, Roger. Stand by on this frequency. Northwest Seven-zero-five, turn right to a heading of three six zero to intercept Jet Forty-one radials.

[*Departure is telling the flight to turn north to intercept another radial of the many radial air routes to and from the airport.*]

Northwest. O.K. And a right turn to three six zero. We're out of . . . ah . . . sixteen now.

[*The flight was at this second still climbing and between 16,000 and 17,000 feet.*]

Tower. Roger, it's heading three six zero.

Northwest. O.K.

TOWER. Northwest Seven-zero-five, contact Miami Center now on one three two point seven.

[*This is a different frequency from the first one. It has been changed because the flight was unable to raise the Center on the former.*]

NORTHWEST. One three two point seven . . . so long.

[*The time: 1:48 P.M. The flight is at this second attempting to reach the Control Center of Miami Air Route Traffic Control and does so . . . identification of the Center being R3A.*]

NORTHWEST. Northwest Seven-oh-five.

TOWER (R3A). Northwest Seven-oh-five, Miami.

NORTHWEST. Northwest Seven-oh-five standing by.

TOWER. Seven-oh-five . . . your present altitude and radial and distance from Miami, please.

NORTHWEST. We're just out of seventeen five on the DME one.

At this second, on this frequency, there occurs a jumble of unintelligible words. But two words stand out reasonably clear —they sound like *Number Two* or *Tank Two.*

What does Number Two mean? What would Tank Two refer to?

Does this mean that the flight has lost its number-two engine? Has it been wrenched from the wings because of the turbulence? Turbulence so severe that Almquist cannot make any turns. (Maybe it's not Feller's voice at all. Could a strange voice have invaded the frequency?) The Air Traffic controller wants clarification of this garbled message, and calls:

"Northwest Seven-oh-five, Miami . . . Northwest Seven-oh-five, Miami . . . Northwest Seven-zero-five, Miami."

But there is no answer from Northwest 705 because the flight is in the cell of the thunderstorm, beneath the towering, forbidding Anvil of the Gods.

At this precise second, when radio communication ceased, Almquist and Feller were fighting not only for their lives but for the lives of the thirty-five passengers and the rest of the terrified crew. The jet was close to 19,500 feet and was pitching and yawing in the grip of violent updrafts. One can only imagine the stark terror in the passenger cabin as the unfortunate travelers were pounded unmercifully by the elements. In fact, from the moment they had taken off they had experienced the terrors of tropical turbulence and never once removed their seat belts. Now, as their modern radar-equipped craft disappeared into the jaws of the storm, they sat in their seats, strapped down like a criminal in an electric chair, hoping for a last-second reprieve.

Gordon Schwan, his wife, and his friends, were still in the Banana Patch of the Shark River. Their luck hadn't progressed any, but the black mass of thunderstorm which they had been watching carefully for some time had. It had moved to the east and was spewing violence—lightning, thunder, and vicious twisting clouds that swirled ahead of the main cloud which stood out black as night.

"I heard my husband shout," said Marilou Schwan. "He was pointing at the storm."

"I looked up from my book and saw a ball of fire, high up in that awful black mass. I thought to myself that the Cubans were attacking, that this fire was a bomb or something. I didn't know what it was and I threw down my book and stood at the rail of the cruiser. We were all very excited and didn't know what to believe. My husband said the fire must have something to do with an airplane.

"The ball of fire came straight down and disappeared from sight behind the jungle. Then there was a terrific explosion.

"We all began chattering together about it. My husband said he heard an explosion or a blast of some kind first and looked up to the clouds and several seconds later he saw the ball of fire.

"Mrs. Mortoff said she heard the blast just as she was taking her fishing rod out of its case. It took her some time to get it out because it was stuck and she had just removed it when she saw the ball of fire.

"We decided to find out then and there how long it was before we saw the fire ball after the blast. Mrs. Mortoff pulled the rod out several times, and every time she did it, we clocked her. It took twelve seconds.

"Therefore, from the time of the first blast to the time of the sighting, it was twelve seconds.

"Next, we all checked our watches to see what time we had. All our watches were different, naturally. Did you ever see two watches alike, let alone six of them? We checked. All of them were between one forty-five and one fifty-five o'clock.

"Next, my husband made two fixes to determine the distance and location of the strange apparition. He figured out that it came down in the swamps between ten and eleven miles away.

"Then, armed with all the information we could get in this forsaken place, we revved up the cruiser and headed back through the Everglades for Whitewater Bay and the distant Flamingo Ranger Station. It took us two hours to make it, and there we turned all our information over to the rangers."

Meanwhile, authorities in Miami waited sixty-eight minutes before instituting a search for the missing jetliner.

"There Are No Survivors"

11

IT WAS A Coast Guard helicopter crew on their last run through the rain and almost out of gas who made the discovery. They were Lieutenant Commander James Dillian and co-pilot William Wallace. Two fires in the darkness of the Everglades acted as beacons while the helicopter circled and then landed. It took only a few seconds to confirm that Flight 705 had been found, and the terse radio message to the outside world startled two cribbage players at Tamiami Airport, headquarters for the search.

"This is Coast Guard Three-oh-four. We have the wreckage in sight . . . it's all busted up . . . consumed by fire."

The helicopter then climbed high above the wreckage while Tamiami operators made a fix. It was latitude 25° 41' north . . . longitude 80° 45' west . . . forty-three miles southwest of Miami International Airport.

Within hours the Civil Aeronautics Board had a team of investigators at Tamiami, aided by agents of the FBI and hundreds of volunteers from the Florida Highway Patrol, the Civil Air Patrol, Everglades Park Rangers, members of the Fresh Water Game and Fish Commission, the Federal Aviation Authority, and sheriff's deputies from Dade and Broward Counties. Their first assignment was to move fourteen miles through snake- and alligator-infested swamp. Helicopters

Helicopters over the Florida Everglades, looking for bodies from a fallen Northwest Airlines 720B jet.

moved the CAB investigators, FBI agents, and newsmen while amphibious vehicles were rounded up for the grim job ahead. By 9:30 P.M. the first team had reached the scene.

In the wet sawgrass near the battered cockpit lay a broken wristwatch. It had stopped at precisely 12:48:42, Central standard time. The CAB report later noted: "The pilots' watches were set to Chicago time."

The first light of morning disclosed that the 720B was scattered over some ten square miles. The entire fuselage, with the exception of the flight deck, had descended at about the same time, struck the soft spongy ground and scattered like a broken melon. The scene looked like a scrap metal yard, the pieces jagged and shattered beyond belief, fire-blackened by the kerosene-fed flames. Inside this mass of torn and twisted metal lay the bodies of twenty-five of the victims, each looking like a poorly molded charcoal sculpture.

Some one hundred yards to the rear of this main fuselage was the tailpiece of the jet, almost intact, with the giant red letters ". . . THWEST . . ." clearly visible on the metal. To either side of the fuselage were the crumpled wings, part of one having looped ahead slightly so that it lay on the sawgrass like an expired silverfish.

Almost half a mile to the front and right of the main wreckage was the flight deck, where the watch and flight recorder were found. Twenty feet away were the bodies of the three-man crew. Near Almquist's body was his brief case, upright, just as though it had been deliberately set down. Nearby was his slide rule, a can of lighter fluid, some flight papers, and a bright red booklet entitled "B720 Ship Manual." There was also a nickel lying in the grass, reflecting the sunlight.

Scattered around for hundreds of yards were the bodies of fifteen victims, visible only from the air and located by the crushing marks in the sawgrass made by their impacting bodies.

There were some survivors of the crash. Fifty tropical fish were still swimming gaily in their water-filled plastic bag. The label read, "Live Tropical Fish." The package was addressed to the Midwest Aquarium in Bensenville, Illinois, and for quick

This five-million-dollar 720B became this worthless pile of junk a few minutes after taking off into a thunderstorm.

delivery the following message was scrawled on the label: "Please phone PO 6-1455."

It took Charles Collar and his CAB squad an entire day just to organize the evidence.

The efficiency with which the investigation at the crash site was conducted was noteworthy, particularly with so many persons involved in the search for the missing pieces. Helicopters picked up the bodies in their plastic shrouds and delivered them to a Seminole schoolyard where they were removed to Miami for identification and embalming. Then seven individual teams of probers went to work assembling the wreckage and laying it out in order of its position in the aircraft. Each fragment was carefully labeled and laid on the broken sawgrass. Helicopters dragged the giant engines back to their relative positions in the debris which now looked like a long, orderly line of jigsaw puzzle pieces. And that's exactly what they were, pieces that stretched for hundreds of yards between the broken nose section and the shattered tail.

As is usual in air crashes of this kind, the CAB was desirous of making a painstaking study of each segment, every rivet, and every bit that had constituted part of the structure, even to the passenger seats and the toilet bowls. To do this required re-creation of the jet. Picked for the location to create this mock-up was the abandoned naval air base of Opa Locka, a few miles west of Miami and five miles northwest of the International Airport. One of the giant hangars there was selected for the job, and the CAB went about fashioning the most extensive mock-up ever built in the history of aviation, and, incidentally, the most expensive.

Twenty years ago, the investigation of an airliner crash cost the CAB around $10,000. But this investigation would cost more than $100,000 even if they were lucky.

This would be the first mock-up in which all the seats would be installed in their rightful positions within the fuselage.

Seven of the nation's top aircraft technicians were given the job of rebuilding the 720B and then finding out what had caused it to break up.

In the Florida Everglades, the CAB investigators extracted bits of metal that once were part of the 720B, and laid them out in order from nose to tail before taking the pieces to another location for reassembly.

Ultra-efficient CAB reconstructed the 720B from scattered bits and pieces. Shown here at a hangar in Opa Locka, Florida, is the frame being made to represent the fuselage and wings of the airliner. (Civil Aeronautics Board photo)

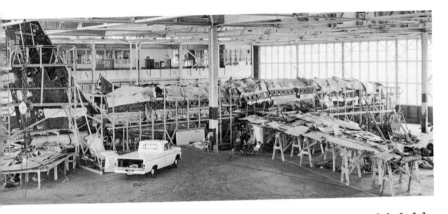

Scraps of metal that were once a proud Boeing jet are labeled by experts and placed on the wooden frame in exact position. The CAB needed to know what caused this new jet to come apart in the air. (Civil Aeronautics Board photo)

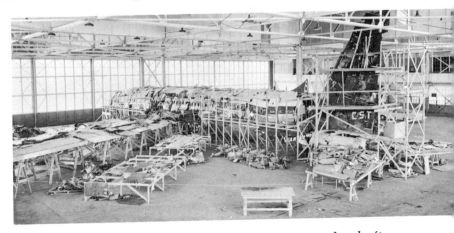

The work of reconstructing the fan jet is almost completed after many months of arduous work. (Civil Aeronautics Board photo)

Ninety-nine per cent of the aircraft parts were located and labeled, and flown from the Everglades to Opa Locka by a team of nine helicopters working round-the-clock for three weeks. Thousands upon thousands of parts were shuttled from the swamps to the hangar and carefully built into place. Soon the jigsaw puzzle began to take shape as the broken pieces were molded into the full-scale model, including the entire center section and the wings.

When the mock-up was completed, the CAB crews wearily regarded the giant jet in the shadows of the hangar looking as though it was all in one piece and ready to fly again. It was a magnificent job of reassembling, and the biggest project in the history of the CAB.

Now to find the cause of the crash.

The technicians on the job called it "The Case of the Many Clues." As things turned out, it was the most intensive crash investigation in airline history.

The flight recorder revealed the ill-fated jet had received 3.1 negative G loads, more downward force on its wings than it was built to withstand.

Not only that, but the flight recorder had some further facts to reveal.

For instance, it disclosed that the climbing speed of the airliner just prior to its breaking up was 8,300 feet per minute, an indication of a tremendous updraft just before the tragedy. One cannot imagine the tremendous forces of nature, forces that could lift a giant of this size upward at more than a mile and a half a minute.

Probers knew there would be an immediate cessation of the updraft, and that all hell would break loose when the jet encountered a downdraft while trimmed for an updraft. The nose would drop and the jet would tumble at more than 600 miles an hour, break up, and cease to be an airplane.

Modern airliners were not stressed to take downloads of this kind, investigators said. Today, jets strike these giant convection currents at speeds for giant liners unheard of and neither measured nor computed fifteen or twenty years ago. Painstaking thunderstorm projects through the years, and particularly

Flight recorder was found in the wreckage of the 720B. Flight recorders, mandatory on U. S. commercial airliners, keep a record of basic flight data such as barometric altitude, indicated air speed, acceleration, compass headings, and elapsed time. Even when smashed to bits, the thin aluminum tape can often be reassembled by the trained scientists of the CAB to provide clues to cause of aircraft disaster.

research done a decade ago, didn't foresee that airliners would swoosh into convection currents with the speed of present-day jets.

While the CAB investigators were working away, sifting clues from autopsies, from the public inquiry, and the reports from voice laboratories, another Boeing 720 jet airliner ran into trouble similar to the Florida episode. It involved the nation's largest airline, one that had pioneered radar storm surveillance in the United States.

On the night of July 12, 1963, United Air Lines Flight 746 from San Francisco to Chicago flew into a combination of weather that provided the crew of six and fifty-three passengers with a never-to-be-forgotten experience. Only superb crewmanship averted a major airline tragedy.

Flight 746 roared off a runway at San Francisco's International Airport at 6:25 P.M. and was scheduled to land at Chicago's O'Hare Field at 12:15 A.M., Central daylight saving time. So that the reader will not be confused, all times will be given in Central daylight saving time.

While on course and operating at the assigned altitude of 37,000 feet over Nebraska, two thirds of the way along its route, the flight entered heavy stratus cloud formations associated with a cold front which was moving across the Great Plains region from the northwest and a warm front which was moving into the same area from the Gulf states. A high-speed jet stream was helping to compound the difficulties of the situation.

The United States Weather Bureau had predicted that on July 12, 1963, there would be a collision of the cold and warm air masses along a lengthy line stretching from Utah, through Colorado, northeastward through Kansas and Nebraska, onward to the north of Chicago and over the northern portion of Michigan.

At 1:15 o'clock that day, the Weather Bureau had issued a general area forecast for the period 7:15 P.M. to 8:09 P.M. which called for: SCATTERED AFTERNOON AND EVENING THUNDER-STORMS OVER EAST SLOPES OF COLORADO AND NEW MEXICO

THROUGH EASTERN OKLAHOMA, WESTERN MISSOURI, WESTERN IOWA, SOUTHWESTERN MINNESOTA WILL INCREASE DURING EVENING WITH THUNDERSTORMS, BECOMING BROKEN IN SHORT LINES AND SPREADING EASTWARD TO CENTRAL WISCONSIN, EASTERN IOWA, EASTERN MISSOURI BY EARLY MORNING.

During the day, a low-pressure area lying over the Canadian province of Manitoba sent cold arctic air in a sweeping counterclockwise motion southwestward over parts of Minnesota, South Dakota and Nebraska. Moving toward this chilly air was the moist humid mass of unstable air from the south and southeast. Long bands of precipitation blanketed a vast area from the Gulf of Mexico to Michigan, and on both sides of the sparring air masses thunderstorms were numerous and sometimes violent.

The situation prompted the Weather Bureau's Severe Local Storms Center at Kansas City to issue a severe-storm warning which bracketed the town of O'Neill, Nebraska, until after 8 P.M. that evening, three hours before the incident. O'Neill was directly on the path of Flight 746.

The surface cold front was located about one hundred miles northwest of O'Neill and was moving slowly southeastward with almost no weather associated with it directly. But squall lines form many miles in advance of such fronts and sometimes, as in this instance, as far as one hundred miles ahead. And this quickly forming squall line was developing directly underneath a jet stream moving west-southwest at 85 knots with the maximum winds over O'Neill at 37,000 feet. The outstanding characteristic of this squall line was the suddenness of its development and dissipation.

Flight 746 was at 37,000 feet.

The moist warm air from the south and southeast was moving into the area at the 5,000-foot level, a factor commonly associated with the development of night thunderstorms. The addition of this unstable air, the jet stream, and other weather factors in the vicinity of O'Neill generated a line of thunderstorms.

Weather Bureau radar reported cloud tops in this region of northeastern Nebraska at 46,000 feet at 11 P.M. that night. This area is one of the most sparsely covered weather reporting areas in the country. The nearest spot weather available at the time was at Sioux Falls, Iowa, one hundred miles away.

The build-up of bad weather was visible to Flight 746 as thick stratus cloud. About 11 P.M., the flight entered the thick cloud and began to experience turbulence, not unusual, as the warm moist air rushed upward to great heights. The FASTEN YOUR SEAT BELTS lights suddenly popped on, and all the passengers, with the exception of one, buckled their belts for what was expected to be a brief spell of moderate turbulence. From time to time the night and the puffy clouds around the aircraft were illuminated by the distant flashes of lightning.

In the flight deck of the United Boeing 720 jet was veteran pilot Captain Lynden E. Duescher, forty-two, of McHenry, Ill. A graduate of the University of Wisconsin, he had begun his flying career in December 1939 for the Morey Airplane Co., of Madison, Wis. He had joined United in 1941, and four years later became one of the first Cargoliner skippers in the country. In September 1945 he became a captain of passenger aircraft, and as of June 24, 1963, had logged an impressive 17,315 hours of flying.

First officer of the flight was Eric Anderson, thirty-four, of Elmhurst, Ill. Second officer was Ervin A. Rochlitz, forty-one, of Oak Lawn, Ill. Also on deck was another United pilot, E. P. Aiken, deadheading for duty in Chicago.

First Officer Anderson had logged 10,200 hours up to this time, while Second Officer Rochlitz had accumulated 10,000 hours. It is apparent that Flight 746 had tremendous flying experience at the controls, and it was a good thing that it did. The aircraft was being flown at this moment by Anderson.

The turbulence now became extreme and the flight asked Air Traffic Control for permission to climb from 37,000 feet to 41,000 feet. This was granted and the sleek jet moved upward through the cloud.

In the plane's G-band iso-echo radar, the flight crew could see a thunderstorm cell at two o'clock position—lying southeast of the airliner at approximately 30 to 35 miles.

Above squall lines fierce updrafts swirling as high as 40,000 feet are common and it is not unusual to experience violent down gusts as far away as 35 miles from the thunderstorms that form along the squall lines. The flight was now experiencing these violent updrafts and what goes up must come down.

The time was precisely 11:14 P.M.

First Officer Anderson was nursing the jet through 37,500 feet when all hell broke loose. Caught in a violent down gust, the airliner nosed over and dived earthward through the cloud, the flight instruments in the cockpit spinning dizzily as the crew fought for control. Flight 746 was completely out of control and diving at tremendous speed. The plane had already experienced severe downloads on its wings when it nosed over, but now it was traveling straight down and the air-speed indicator went crazy. The indicator climbed to 450 knots, at which time the speed went off the flight recorder. For an unbelievable fourteen seconds the airliner dived at a speed so great that it could not be recorded on the flight recorder. The jet broke the sound barrier, sending a double shock wave toward the ground. But the wings held and the plane did not spin over on its back.

At 26,000 feet, the jet with its fifty-six panicking passengers and numbed crew broke through the cloud, and the pilots were able to orient themselves with a ground reference. Strapped to their seats with shoulder harnesses—which probably saved their lives—they tried to bring the hurtling airliner under control. They did this by reducing power, using wing spoilers and flaps to try and maneuver the jet. By bringing it into a shallow dive so as not to rip off the wings, the crew were at last able, at 14,000 feet, to regain control . . . but they had fallen over five miles at a speed that often exceeded the sound barrier.

On reaching Chicago several of the passengers were given first-aid treatment, mostly for shock. The three stewardesses of the flight, Annette Mancini, of Franklin Park, Ill., Connie Atma, Des Plaines, Ill., and Nancy Mitchell, Schiller Park, Ill., received brief medical check-ups. The crew, though badly shaken by the experience, were not injured, nor did they require medical attention.

The passenger whose seat belt had not been fastened was

Robert E. Walter, of Baltimore, Md. Reports merely identified him as a soldier, but if he is as lucky on the ground as he was in the air, he'll live out his regulation life span. By holding on to the seat rests with all his might, he had been able to stay in position and was not hurled to the rear of the plunging airliner.

To say that the Civil Aeronautics Board was interested in the incident would be putting it mildly. The behavior of the Boeing 720 was just too similar to the Miami 720B pattern to be overlooked. The CAB seized the flight recorder, and the jetliner was grounded by the Federal Aviation Authority. The aircraft underwent thorough inspection. No structural damage was found, and the plane was released to service.

Is the Past Prologue?   12

ELSEWHERE in the United States and in the world, the storms continued to take their deadly toll.

A United Arab Airlines twin-engined passenger plane with thirty-four passengers aboard took off from Cairo for Alexandria in a raging storm, broke up after several minutes in the air, and fell in a shower of flame and debris into the village of Zahwein, killing all on board. A Pan-American 707 was struck by lightning over the North Atlantic and had to return to England because its radar dome had been knocked out. A Trans-Canada Air Lines *Vanguard* over the Rockies and en route to Edmonton in a cold front hit a violent downdraft that almost wrenched its wings loose. Arriving at Edmonton one passenger was dead and more than a score were rushed to the hospital with cuts and bruises. A Tag Airlines De Havilland *Dove* escaped with seven holes in its fuselage when it was struck by lightning between Detroit and Cleveland on March 13. A National Airlines *Electra* carrying forty-four passengers was struck and damaged by lightning while flying through a storm over Snow Hill, Maryland.

But not all flights were as fortunate as these last three.

For several days the weather over New York State had been hot and humid with temperatures in the Rochester area climb-

The Vickers Vanguard, *a huge turboprop airliner, is an outgrowth of the successful* Viscount. *It is flown in North America by Air Canada (formerly Trans-Canada Air Lines). Like all turboprops, it is extremely dependable.* (Trans-Canada Air Lines photo)

ing over the 90-degree mark, moderated slightly by the vastness of Lake Ontario on its northern boundary. A slow-moving cold front from northern Canada was predicted by the weather forecasters in Cleveland. This front was traveling in a southeasterly direction and was expected to move into New York State at approximately 4 P.M., Eastern standard time on Tuesday, July 2, 1963.

Severe storm warnings were posted from Buffalo on the west, to as far east as the state of Vermont, with the possibility of severe local thunderstorms, high winds, hail and the chance of two or three tornadoes. This weather forecast was typical of all such cold fronts moving into hot and unstable air conditions. And the prediction proved to be correct, with the exception that no tornadoes were reported.

A squall line associated with this front formed southeast of Rochester Airport during the midafternoon and went charging across New York State and into Pennsylvania before exhausting itself against the mountains.

The cold front moved in behind the squall line, black and dangerous and rumbling with earth-shaking thunder and blinding lightning bolts. At 3:45 P.M., the swirling black storm was lying northwest of the Rochester Airport, while at the terminal a Mohawk Airlines Martin 404, a twin-engined 40-passenger airliner, was moving to the east end of the field for a take-off which was supposed to send it to White Plains, New York, and thence to Newark, New Jersey.

The aircraft was loaded with forty passengers and a crew of three. At the controls sat Capt. Richard M. Dennis, thirty-nine, a pilot with more than ten years with Mohawk and a man familiar with the Martin 404. A former World War II pilot, he resided in Fairview, New Jersey, with his wife and four children. His co-pilot for the day was Jon W. Neff, thirty-three, of Wilmington, Delaware. His stewardess was Mary Ann Miara, nineteen, of Sayreville, New Jersey.

Captain Dennis scanned the storm clouds that blotted out the sky. Some of his passengers later described them as "black as night." He apparently decided that if he could make a left-hand turn after the take-off, he could avoid the storm bearing down on the field. He called the Rochester Tower, requesting permission to take off and make the left turn. The Tower replied: "Mohawk One-one-two, you're cleared to a left turn on course . . ."

Captain Dennis released the brakes of the 20-ton plane and it began to gather speed down the west runway. The time was 3:49 P.M. Passengers later reported that hail was bouncing off the wings. The aircraft lifted from the concrete into the heavy rain and swirling winds of an apparent wind shift which is common to all such thunderstorms. Unable to struggle further, the aircraft faltered, the left wing dipped. The plane nosed over and plunged from about eighty feet into the soft mud at the end of the runway, splitting open like a ripe watermelon. Miraculously it did not explode. The engines broke loose and skidded over the ground, one of them steamed to a stop fifty feet away while the other continued on for another fifty feet.

Captain Dennis and his co-pilot died in the wreckage. So did five of the passengers. The failure of the aircraft to explode saved the lives of the others. The downpour of rain was so intense that it probably staved off ignition of the ruptured fuel cells, and, when a spark finally appeared, firemen were on hand to douse the flames. This marked the first fatal accident for Mohawk, a local service carrier operating from as far west as Detroit, north to Toronto and throughout New York State down to New Jersey. Thirty-five passengers and the stewardess were injured, some with minor cuts and bruises, others critically.

The public inquiry into the Mohawk disaster began in Rochester on Tuesday, August 20, and lasted four full days.

Since CAB investigation had indicated there was no mechanical failure in the aircraft, the inquiry settled around the weather and the manner in which modern weather reports are gathered, distributed, and—sometimes neglected.

On that particular day of July 2, 1963, one thing stood out clearly: The weather was severe and obviously dangerous that day in the vicinity of Rochester, just as had been predicted well in advance by the U. S. Weather Bureau at Cleveland.

Mohawk Captain Herbert H. Holmes, forty, of West Peabody, Massachusetts, testified at the inquiry that the stormy weather over Lake Ontario that day created a pattern on his radar "so large that it scared me . . . it was the largest I had ever observed on radar."

Holmes, who was flying on Mohawk's recently opened route from Toronto to Buffalo, testified that he changed his course to avoid "two mammoth squall lines" and, being a competent pilot, he radioed Mohawk's communication center at Utica at 3:45 P.M., alerting the center to the dangerous weather pattern. When he landed in Buffalo, he said he telephoned Mohawk's dispatcher in Utica, Charles J. McIntyre, at 4 P.M. about his "in-flight" report, to impress on him the severity of the storm.

Holmes said that McIntyre replied: "What in-flight report?"

On May 20, 1964, the CAB determined the probable cause of this accident was the loss of control during an attempted takeoff into a severe thunderstorm.

"The failure of the captain to properly appraise the weather conditions and his attempted takeoff into a severe thunderstorm raises serious doubt as to his judgment," the report concluded.

Elsewhere the CAB was having a difficult task attempting to determine the cause of an appalling disaster over the northwest Pacific Coast.

On Monday, June 3, 1963, a Northwest Orient Airlines DC-7, chartered by the Military Air Transport Service to carry soldiers and their families from McCord Air Force Base in Washington to Anchorage, Alaska, fell into the sea.

This was one of the most horrible disasters in the history of flying. It sent 101 men, women, and children hurtling to their deaths. Like most airline disasters at sea, the true cause may never be known.

The CAB sent a team of investigators into the area, located some sixty miles north of the northern tip of the Queen Charlotte Islands of British Columbia. Clues were indeed meager. A few broken bodies were found and these were rushed to autopsy tables. Debris was found floating for miles around, but the main wreckage was at the bottom of the ice-cold Pacific and would never be recovered because of the tremendous depths to which it had plunged. What few parts were recovered were taken to Ketchikan Airport, 175 miles northeast of the crash site.

The CAB hoped that modern scientific detection methods might help pinpoint the cause.

Was it weather? Newspapers said No, but newspapers aren't always right. "Weather was discounted as a factor," said an Associated Press dispatch from Juneau, Alaska. Actual conditions indicate the contrary.

Weather reports for the area that day showed clouds and precipitation up to some 16,000 feet and icing conditions had been forecast at 14,000 feet—the very level to which the DC-7 had been assigned. At 16,000 feet there was a temperature variation which could melt ice and at 18,000 feet the weather was clear.

Captain Albert F. Olsen, veteran Northwest pilot, was cruising at 14,000 feet when he undoubtedly entered the icing area and probably encountered turbulence. This is borne out by the fact that several seats fished from the water had seat belts buckled, indicating turbulence. Captain Olsen radioed the Canadian Department of Transport radio station at Queen Charlotte at 10:06 A.M. and asked for clearance to 18,000 feet. He wanted to get up and out of the trouble.

The traffic controller took several minutes to study the request because of other air traffic. There was another plane just above the Northwest DC-7 and it was flying in the clear at 18,000 feet. Beneath it were the deep forbidding clouds in which Olsen was encased.

The 16,000-foot corridor was found to be clear of aircraft and there was a good chance that ice on the DC-7 would melt at that altitude. Therefore, the controller decided to give Olsen this new height and he called the flight on the radio.

There was no response.

In those few minutes, maybe not more than three or four minutes at the most, the flight was dead or dying.

Investigation of the broken parts showed that the aircraft had probably broken up in the air and a tremendous explosion of fuel resulted. Wreckage was blown over a square mile of water.

The first thought that occurred to investigators when they were informed that 101 persons were aboard the aircraft was whether or not the flight was overloaded. They learned that it was not. Its allowable weight at take-off from McCord had been determined at 127,558 pounds. According to the records, the actual weight at take-off was 123,171 pounds, well under the maximum allowable.

Whatever happened to the flight was swift and unpredictable, and it was certainly catastrophic. The CAB was not able to determine the cause after a year's investigation.

During the early morning of Sunday, July 28, 1963, a modern Mark IV *Comet* jet airliner of the United Arab Airlines tangled with a monsoon thunderstorm near Bombay with disastrous results. There were 62 people on board, including a crew of eight and twenty-six Boy Scouts from the Philippines en route to a jamboree at Marathon, near Athens. All of them perished in the tragedy that was similar in every respect to the crash of a *Comet* more than a decade earlier at Calcutta in another monsoon storm.

The *Comet* was flying from Tokyo to Cairo, and it is normal for the aircraft to cross over Bombay's Santa Cruz Airport and head out over the sea on its western side to begin descending for the final approach and landing. The flight did so on this occasion, crossing above the airport at 1:51 A.M. (Indian standard time) under the watchful eye of the airport radar controller.

Heavy downpours of rain were lashing the area and lightning bolts of fierce intensity made filigree of the cloud castles as the sleek jet began its descent through the cloud layers. The final act in the drama occurred a few minutes later. Fisher-

Awe-inspiring anvil of typical cumulo-nimbus cloud thunderstorm.

men on Madh Island in the Mada Islands group, thirty miles west of Bombay Harbor, were awakened by a loud explosion and the noise of their dogs barking and howling. Tumbling from their crude huts along the beach, they saw a "powerful flash of light plunging downward into the sea."

Like many other tragedies over the water, this one would be difficult to solve, and yet the events fit a pattern of mixing airliners and storms and picking up the pieces.

Flags at the Marathon Boy Scout jamboree flew at half mast the next day so that 14,000 Scouts from eighty-three nations would remember.

The year of 1963 was fast establishing a record for disasters despite the modernization of equipment and facilities both in the air and on the ground.

The next episodes took place in southern France. On Wednesday, August 14, 1963, another tragedy occurred with a familiar aircraft and a familiar thunderstorm. Only the names were different.

On this day, the weather was beastly from the Scandinavian peninsula to the northern shores of the sparkling Mediterranean Sea. A broad trough of low pressure covered the British Isles, the North Sea, and the Baltic communities. Associated with this low-pressure system was a typical cold front running through northern Spain northeastward through central France and into Switzerland. Along this cold front, thunderstorms and shower activity dominated the weather.

A new feeder airline had just been established in France and its first flight was to tangle with this front. Air France and the French Railways had agreed to set up a feeder airline service from the larger interior cities to the busy short-haul vacation resorts along the Mediterranean. The new airline would be called Air Inter Company.

A fleet of seven *Viscount* aircraft were to be the hub of the new internal air service. Unfortunately, the new system got off to a poor start. One of the *Viscounts* took off from Lille for the short hop to Lyons with sixteen persons aboard, including the crew of three. The flight was uneventful until a few seconds after the pilot radioed that he was beginning his descent toward the Lyons Airport. He was, at this time, only fifteen miles north of the field. The aircraft entered a thunderstorm and some witnesses thought they saw it struck by a lightning bolt, but only investigation would be able to determine this.

The *Viscount* hurtled toward the ground, flattened out, and struck a farmhouse roof, instantly killing a small boy standing outside the house. The plane broke into many pieces, scattering bits and bodies over the sodden fields. Twelve in the plane died, including the crew. Two women and two children escaped with critical injuries.

Then, on the night of September 12, 1963, thirty-six British tourists clambered aboard a chartered twin-engined *Viking* airliner for a four-hour trip to Perpignan, France. The weather was unusually balmy and the tourists, including a young couple who had just been married, were eagerly looking forward to the trip and the rewards beyond. There were 10 married couples aboard, nine single girls, one matron, and six men.

The aircraft was operated by a Paris charter company, called Air-Nautic. Its crew was comprised of Captain Max Dunoyer, First Officer Leopold Marold, Navigator Emile Jamin, and stewardess Muriel Tiberghain.

Shortly after 9:30 P.M., the *Viking* groaned into the skies, loaded with forty persons for the 630-mile flight.

Although the weather that night of September 12 was delightful over England, it was anything but good over Perpignan. A low-pressure area was moving southeast over central Spain and the clash of warm air being hoisted into the lofty regions of the Pyrenees was creating violent thunderstorms over a wide area along the very path that the chartered flight was to follow. Violent winds and hailstorms were reported in the area at the time that the flight was scheduled to arrive over Perpignan.

Captain Dunoyer radioed the airport controller and reported that he was preparing to land soon and was fighting bad weather. The next episode in the drama took place on the slopes of a lonely ravine deep in the heart of the mountains beneath snow-covered Pic de Roquette.

A lonely shepherd, huddled with his flock beneath the raging storm, heard a thunderous noise near by that was so unusual he decided to race with the news to the village of Py and tell the local gendarme. He had no watch and he had no idea of the time.

However, a mountain game warden, Marcel Marchant, saw a flash of fire in the storm which could not have been created by lightning, and he too decided to brave the storm and inform the authorities. His watch read 1:30 A.M. The British charter flight was to have landed at that moment at Perpignan, almost fifty miles to the northeast, an indication that the aircraft was off course and may have been blown away by the violent winds, compounded by the lack of navigational aids and weather reports in this lonely region. Two other airliners flying toward Perpignan at this time were diverted to other airports, near Toulouse, because of the storm.

A French Air Force plane first sighted the wreckage at the 5,000-foot level on the northern slopes of Pic de Roquette. The tailpiece was clearly visible through the broken clouds that swirled along the peaks.

A crack team of French and British investigators moved into the camp in an attempt to learn the cause of the disaster. But the superstitious mountain people already knew the answer. It was Friday the thirteenth.

Strangely enough, after an airplane disaster the public, and airline passengers in particular, seems to forget the tragedy. After two days, it is all but forgotten so far as the nation is concerned—about four or five days in the city or area close to the scene, and about a week or ten days in the towns and villages where the victims lived. Relatives and next-of-kin, however, never forget. At least, this is the usual state of affairs.

In the case of the Northwest 720B disaster in the Everglades, however, the public interest, particularly in the Greater Miami area, continued for several weeks, and newspapers were beset

This is all that remained of the proud British Viking airliner that was en route to Mediterranean holiday resorts.

with letters from their readers. Most of the writers were frankly curious as to why, with all the modern facilities at its disposal, a modern jet airliner should crash. They were as concerned with why the crash had occurred as with what had caused it. Some columnists tried to explain that the big jets fly so fast that, by the time the pilots see the turbulent areas in their radar sets, they are already into the turbulence, and the long delays in getting route changes only compound the situation.

Some of the letters to the editors were indeed interesting.

Two, representing divergent points of view, are reproduced here from the Miami *Herald,* whose coverage of the disaster was exemplary.

Editor, *The Herald:* As a passenger on 18 flights, made within 22 months with different airlines and on different kinds of aircraft, I watched with much interest the TV reports about the Everglades disaster and read with much interest the various articles about this tragic affair.

The fact that usually the final decision whether or not to start any flight rests with the pilot is good and bad at the same time. I believe that better arrangements could be made in order to increase the safety of air traffic.

The pilot should have the unrestricted right to cancel any given flight if the meteorological conditions are such that he considers the flight too hazardous to undertake.

He should not have the right to decide to start the flight.

There should be a three-man committee on airport duty 24 hours a day composed of an expert in meteorology, a representative of the airlines (there is certainly some kind of association in which all commercial airlines are represented), and an official of the Federal Aviation Agency or the Civil Aeronautics Board. Such a committee should release the airplane for each individual flight not more than 15 minutes before the starting time, if the conditions seem to be appropriate.

The pilot should have no authority to start any flight without release of such a committee, but he should be authorized to cancel the flight in spite of the release of the committee.

The airlines should include in their general conditions—and this should be approved by the competent Federal Authority—a clause entitling them to cancel any flight on account of adverse meteorological conditions, without being subject to claims for indemnification by any passenger who might miss an important engagement by such late cancellation.

If a pilot cancels a flight for such reason, this might be recorded, but without recording the pilot's name, in order to avoid that one pilot or another gets a "black eye" for such cancellations.

Such an arrangement can easily be made. It would save money for airlines and insurance companies, and, much more important, it would save many lives.

Ernesto Gerothwohl

Editor, *The Herald*: I was shocked and dismayed to find on the front page of *The Herald*, this headline: TRAGIC QUESTION: WHAT TURNED JET INTO BALL OF FIRE?

And underneath that, several distortions or outright false and misleading statements.

I have been a pilot for 23 years and have been an airline pilot for the last 17.

My airline flying for these years has been through the Caribbean and Central and South America. I have been flying four-engine jets.

This area has thunderstorms of a number and intensity hardly equalled any place on earth. It would be safe to say that in more than 15,000 hours of flying, I have flown through more than 2,000 thunderstorms, and I can certify that the jet aircraft we are flying today is far safer than any which has previously been designed.

Therefore, it is strange to me, that the *Herald* should resort to sensational journalism and misleading statements such as that written by Mr. E. V. W. Jones in his article.

Mr. Jones says in his article that the big four-engine jet could easily have been torn asunder by a thunderstorm's turbulence.

If I believed this, I would resign my job today.

The Boeing 720 underwent one of the most strenuous testing programs ever conducted on a commercial aircraft. The gust loads it might encounter in the most severe turbulence were computed and the aircraft carefully stressed to withstand them.

Further, at the time of the incident involving Northwest Flight 705, the aircraft, according to its radio message, was in a climb. In this configuration, the air speed would be slower than cruising and the likelihood of damage from turbulence even less than under cruising conditions.

Your Mr. Jones further states, "Thunderstorms are fully capable of shearing the wings off a plane in flight. The violent turbulence, the tremendous up and down drafts in these storms is beyond belief, except to pilots who have experienced them. Snapped wings and ripped wing fuel tanks might easily result in an explosion like that witnessed by Schwan and his fishing friends."

Such statements are misleading and undermine the faith of the public in aviation.

Certainly, here in Miami, where such a great segment of the population depends on aviation for its livelihood, such sensational and irresponsible journalism is to be deplored.

Julian H. Braswell

In the brief period of time between November 29, 1963, and February 18, 1964, there occurred three jet disasters that took 256 lives. The first was near Montreal, Canada; the second near Elkton, Maryland; and the third at New Orleans, Louisiana.

These crashes involved modern aircraft that cost between 5 million and 7.5 million dollars apiece. Two of the crashes occurred only a few minutes after take-off at night, while the third happened while the airliner was circling in a holding pattern awaiting the chance to land.

These events took place over a time when daily newspapers in the United States and Canada were running a series of air-safety articles that promised death immunity of 99.99978 per cent.

Although the causes of the crashes have not yet been definitely established, preliminary investigation has revealed that each one occurred during stormy weather in the vicinity of a rampaging cold front. Whether or not the storms caused all three will not be known until the investigations are completed, and in one case there is a good chance that the cause will never be known because the airliner, incredible as it may seem, did not have a flight recorder aboard.

The first in the tragic series was the plunge of a brand-new DC-8F owned and operated by Air Canada, at that time called Trans-Canada Air Lines. The plane carried 111 passengers and seven crew members to their death, the worst air disaster in

Canada's history and the second worst jet crash in the world. The jet was piloted by Captain John Snider of Toronto, a flier with nineteen years of perfect flying to his credit.

On Friday night, November 29, 1963, Capt. Snider wheeled the huge Douglas Cargo-Liner onto the rain-slick runways of Montreal's International Airport for the short 315-mile hop westward to Toronto, in the first leg of a transcontinental flight to Vancouver. The four Pratt & Whitney fan-jet engines roared to full life and in less than a minute lifted 213,000 pounds into the stormy skies northeast of the sprawling airport.

"Flight Eight-three-one off at six twenty-four," First Officer Harry Dyck radioed the Montreal controller. His next report was due to be made in another minute or so as the flight passed the 3,000-foot level. The airliner roared into the low scud clouds and could be seen only on the airport's surveillance radar. At 3,000 feet, Dyck radioed the expected report. He was told to call again when the aircraft had passed through 7,000 feet. Dyck confirmed the instruction.

The jet, climbing upward through the storm, was heading north and its crew were preparing to turn westward and then southwestward for the final course of the flight. Torrential rain may have prevented the Montreal radar from "seeing" the next episode.

The horror of the next few seconds was witnessed almost alone by Noel Aubertin, the parish police officer of Sainte Thérèse de Blainville, a village located sixteen miles north-northwest of Montreal in the foothills of the Laurentian Mountains.

Aubertin first heard the mighty roar of the jet engines high overhead in the storm. He looked up and then froze. The noise, growing louder, seemed to be rushing at him from all sides and the next thing he heard was an earth-shaking explosion. A dazzling column of flame leaped 500 feet into the sky as 51,000 pounds of JP4 aviation fuel caught fire.

TCA Flight 831 was dead. Its final convulsive efforts buried its heaviest parts some sixty feet below the surface of the sodden ground. The tremendous crater made by the impact soon filled with water and then froze over.

The CAB in Washington rushed a team of experts to the Canadian scene to assist in the investigation. They believed they could see a parallel in the crash of a DC-8 off Portugal two years earlier. The wreckage seemed to fit a pattern. The angle of descent seemed to be fairly identical. And the weather had a strange similarity. Careful study of the weather reports for that night indicated the possibility of a wind shear at 6,000 feet which could have proved lethal to a jet airliner climbing and turning upward through the turbulent zone. Such wind shears had already caused plenty of trouble with jets, as the CAB team knew.

It was the giant DC-8F that carried no flight recorder; thus, the probable cause of the crash may never be established. The destruction was so complete that many months after the tragedy investigators were still digging for clues behind a steel cofferdam.

Ten days after this frightful accident, a Pan American 707, circling beneath a violent thunderstorm in a holding area south and west of Philadelphia, in the vicinity of Elkton, Maryland, was struck by lightning. There was an immediate explosion of fuel, and the aircraft—the first 707 to go into commercial service in the world—plunged to the earth, carrying eighty persons to their deaths.

The torn left wing of the plane was located two miles east of the main wreckage, indicating that it had parted from the airliner while in flight, although there was no indication that the plane had encountered severe turbulence. Despite the arguments that raged over the CAB preliminary findings, the culprit appeared to have been a lightning bolt. It was associated with a thunderstorm that had been accurately predicted before the disaster. The ill-fated Clipper had taken off from Baltimore's Friendship Airport at 8:25 P.M. for the short hop to Philadelphia into an area already well-stocked with planes awaiting their chance to get through the storms for their landings.

A flight that was to have taken only twenty minutes had accepted eternity as its destination, and many would ask: Why all the rush?

This is the Pan Am Clipper that went down in flames at Elkton, Maryland, in December 1963. This photograph was taken on an earlier and historic occasion, for this was the second plane to roll off the Boeing assembly lines at Renton, Washington. It was the first jet delivered to Pan Am. (Boeing Airplane Company photo)

At the time of the lightning strike on the Pan Am Clipper, it was thought that the co-pilot calmly reported that his plane was going down in flames. The recording of this voice was broadcast all over the world—the voice of a courageous pilot giving the details of his death as he went to meet it. Newspapers and wire services were quick to pick up this dramatic tidbit.

But such was not the case.

The voice heard through the storm was that of Captain Gerald Sutliff, co-pilot of a National Airlines DC-8 jet flying 1,000 feet above the Clipper. It was he who reported: "Clipper Two-fourteen is going down in flames." He had no sooner said this than his own jet was struck by lightning and the bolt tore the static wicks off at the wingtips. The Pan Am 707 had carried no wicks.

A short time after the Pan Am crash, the CAB recommended that all 707 aircraft be equipped with static wicks. Later the Federal Aviation Agency issued an airworthiness directive requiring increased protection from lightning for outboard wing sections of Boeing 707 and 720 aircraft around the fuel vent surge tanks.

This was in April 1964 and, at the time of the order, lightning struck the top and bottom antennas of a United Air Lines *Viscount* on which Mrs. Lyndon B. Johnson was a passenger. Later in the same week an Eastern Air Lines *Constellation* was struck on the number-four engine while flying near Washington in thunderstorms. Neither aircraft was damaged.

An old wives' tale has it that disaster strikes in threes. Coincidentally, a third jet disaster occurred soon after these other two crashes. On February 25, 1964, an Eastern Air Lines DC-8 jet, climbing through cloud-filled skies above New Orleans International Airport, disappeared from the tower's radar surveillance scope. The airliner plunged earthward, burying itself beneath the bottom ooze of Lake Pontchartrain with fifty-eight hapless victims, some of them small children.

Again the CAB investigators thought they saw a strange similarity with the Portugal and the Montreal crashes: the Eastern plunge and scattering of wreckage seemed to be almost iden-

A Douglas DC-8 like this one plunged to the muddy bottom of Lake Ponchartrain. When the flight recorder was finally pulled to the surface by a clam crane, probers found it to be so severely damaged as to be well-nigh useless in assisting the investigation. (Douglas Aircraft Company photo)

tical to the Portugal incident. It was certainly beginning to look as if jet disasters in storms were following a pattern. Could they be predictable?

There was considerable debate as to whether or not the Eastern jet had encountered severe turbulence in the storm clouds over Louisiana. The pilot had not reported turbulence. But the CAB was tracking down a report that the pilot of another jet airliner, which had taken off from the New Orleans' runways two minutes after the Eastern flight, found moderate to severe turbulence at approximately the same height the Eastern jet had reached before diving to the ground.

The violent storms of the skies, particularly those at night, were taking their toll with grisly abandon.

When was it all going to stop?

If this book, *Anvil of the Gods,* gives pilots a greater awareness of the destructive power of thunderstorms, its publication has been worthwhile.

If this mass of evidence (and this is only part of it) cannot convince jet pilots flying commercial aircraft of the danger of flying into thunderstorms, perhaps they should not be flying.

Appendix:

The U. S. Air Force and Thunderstorms

IT WOULD BE UNFAIR to conclude that only the commercial airlines have been plagued by thunderstorms, icing, and hail conditions. A goodly portion of the experience has been shared by military planes and some of the more frightening episodes were detailed in *Aerospace Safety* Magazine for June 1963, under a broad feature on thunderstorms with a single bold word beginning and ending the comprehensive report . . . the word *DON'T*.

In this article the Air Force picked out the effects of thunderstorm flying on various aircraft types to show other pilots the dangers that exist to all kinds of aircraft now in service.

The following report was made by the pilot of an F-102 jet fighter:

"We had two severe weather warning areas to deal with, the first in the immediate area. We planned to climb VFR around the first one, and then thread our way through the tops of the second.

"We did fine on the climbout, and were in pretty good shape at 42,000 when we approached the second warning area.

"About four minutes after I reported passage VFR on top at 42,000, we encountered moderate turbulence, and my engine suffered a compressor stall. I retarded the throttle and lowered the nose, and fought a series of compressor stalls that followed, one after another. In doing so, I realized that I was falling into some pretty rough weather. I managed to recover at 36,000 feet, and so notified the Center. They advised me of commercial traffic at 30,000 in the area, so I called for a left turn of the flight.

"About then, one of my wingmen called to say that he too had suffered a compressor stall, and was now flamed out. I told him to do as he saw fit, and to hold whatever altitude he could.

"Immediately following this transmission I hit the most severe turbulence I have ever experienced. Its force was such that my aircraft flamed out in an inverted position.

"I stopcocked the throttle and switched to emergency AC power, and managed a recovery at about 30,000 feet. Immediately thereafter, my emergency AC power failed. I don't know whether I also lost both hydraulic systems, since I switched my attention to the turn and bank indicator. The turbulence was so severe that I could only hope to 'hold on' and ride it out. I couldn't even hold myself in the upright position. Among other things, my head struck the optical gunsight. I developed what seemed to be a left-hand spin, and lost altitude very rapidly. Approaching 10,000 feet, I ejected.

"The automatic opening devices worked properly, and I found myself in the middle of a hailstorm. My helmet departed in the process, and my face was beaten rather severely by the hail. My descent was both slow and turbulent, taking some 20 minutes to complete.

"On two occasions, I oscillated so severely that I found myself above the canopy, which promptly collapsed. When I fell again, the canopy would reopen.

"The landing was complicated by high winds and severe oscillations but I sustained very minor injuries."

The pilot of a T-33 twin-seat jet trainer described his own frightful encounter with a thunderstorm:

"I took off and stayed VFR until we'd gone about 10 miles west of Oke City and then climbed up through the overcast, as specified by our IFR clearance, to get on top. At 21,000 feet we were not on top and the radio static was very bad. I tried but could not contact Oklahoma City Radio.

"At about 24,000 feet we were suddenly in very, very dark clouds. We had been flying on instruments without cockpit lights, but now they were necessary. This was about 1920 hours, and we were starting to get what we then considered to be thunderstorm turbulence.

"The instruments were steady as a rock. We were climbing at about 240 knots and both turn and bank gyro horizon were as they should be. However, the rate-of-climb pegged itself at 6000 feet per minute, UP! We could feel the tremendous updraft.

"I had both my hands on the stick and had my harness and belt tightened up, expecting very shortly to hit a downdraft and then be in the clear.

"At this time the airplane suddenly snap-rolled to the right and then continued into a series of very violent snaps, first to the right and then to the left. Next we found ourselves in what appeared to be a crazy twirling-motion maneuver. Incidentally, we definitely were not spinning; a twirling or twisting motion is the only way I can describe it. Strangely enough the instruments were still indicating normal except for the rate of climb and the altimeter. The latter was showing a decided drop in altitude, although the rate of climb was still holding at 6000 feet, UP! I couldn't understand how there could be such a tremendous pressure change so quickly.

"Along with the twirling motion, we were still getting those violent snaps that threw us around in the cockpit. This was certainly the strangest maneuver I'd ever been in, and I've flown through many thunderstorms.

"The pilot in the rear cockpit asked me if I thought we should blow the canopy and said he thought we had received some structural damage to the aircraft. After a few seconds I answered him and said, 'Van, I think you'd better blow the canopy if this continues, you get out of the airplane whenever you want to.'

"Somehow, he was able to reach up against the tremendous G forces and actuate the canopy jettison system. The moment this was done, we lost our helmets and oxygen masks. This was between 20,000 and 25,000 feet.

"We were still experiencing this twirling motion; then the plane would suddenly snap and keep snapping. I was fighting the controls and trying to fly the plane when it suddenly flamed out. This was undoubtedly due to the tremendous negative G forces that we were being subjected to.

"The airplane was starting to break up and the hail was absolutely terrific in the cockpit. My face was being cut to ribbons. I couldn't see much, since my right eye was closed and the left one was simply a slit. I could just barely make out one or two of the instruments. We were unable to communicate with each other now, but I felt sure that Van was getting out. At about 10,000 feet there was a momentary lull in the turbulence and I sensed that Van was out of the airplane.

"I now tried to eject myself but was unable to get my right hand off the stick and over onto the ejection seat handle. The centrifugal forces were so great that I just couldn't move in that cockpit. My left hand was still on the throttle, my feet were on the rudder pedals and I could not move them. Finally, I managed to get my right hand into a position where I could reach and catch hold of the seat handle.

"I pulled upon the handle and immediately was blown out of the cockpit without ever squeezing the ejection seat trigger, to my knowledge.

"As I hit the slipstream, the seat was torn off and I thought then that it had ripped off my parachute, too. I knew that I was tumbling violently and felt sure that I was falling to my death for I just knew that the parachute had been carried away with the seat.

"The rain and hail sort of brought me to clearer consciousness for a few seconds and a tremendous flash of lightning revealed that my ripcord was hanging by my left side. I reached for the D ring, pulled it and was the most surprised man in the world when I suddenly felt a terrific tug on my shoulders as my parachute opened.

"I started floating now, instead of falling, and the chute

stopped a lot of the hail from cutting my face and beating into my eyes. However, the turbulence of the air kept me swinging in great arcs of about 180 degrees and the parachute was so wet that it would collapse as I was swung from one side to the other and then would puff open as I'd hit the bottom of each wild swing. Because of the turbulence, the chute started to twist and twirl, and fight as I would, I couldn't do a thing about it. At this point I firmly believed I'd never come out of this nightmare alive.

"Suddenly my feet slammed into the ground, followed immediately by the rest of my body. This, of course, was no controlled landing, and I had the wind knocked out on impact. It felt as though a Missouri mule had just kicked me in the back.

"In a couple of moments I got back a bit of wind and tried to stand up. Just as I staggered to my feet, the wind in howling fury snatched the parachute, and for the next minute or two I was dragged first one way and then the other. I didn't have a quick-release harness and probably wouldn't have been able to use it anyway, unless it had been a chest type.

"I finally managed to release the chest strap and right leg snap and then was able to slide out of the harness. I stood up and was gratified to find that I could walk, but it was a supreme effort, believe me."

Next, one of the surviving passengers of a C-118 military transport airliner told his brief but dramatic remembrance of a thunderstorm encounter which took the lives of forty-six other persons:

"Shortly after take-off we felt a downdraft. It pulled me against the seat belt and caused loose bags, hats and papers to be forced against the top of the aircraft. It seemed that we had a momentary electrical failure. The lights dimmed at that particular instant. It was the most tremendous downdraft I have ever felt. It stopped and everyone assumed that we were going to continue on our way. The fellow next to me said, 'That was quite a downdraft.' I agreed. The next instant—not more than three seconds later—we hit another downdraft. It felt as if we were entering turbulence. My head was forced back against the seat. We were decelerating with forward momentum. There then was a blank."

The following is a brief report of what happens to a modern jet fighter when struck by lightning while climbing up through a storm. The plane was an F-104. The report reads:

"During the climbout the aircraft was struck by lightning. A loud explosion was heard and an extremely bright flash observed. The explosion occurred at the same time that the throttle was moved from after-burner range to military. First thought was that a compressor stall had occurred, but engine instruments disclosed engine operation to be normal. However, three strip panel lights were on: instruments on emergency power, DC monitor bus out and APC out. All Navaids and the UHF radio immediately became inoperative. Subsequent examination disclosed that the nose radome had sustained a one-eighth inch hole on the top side and paint was chipped over a four-inch area. Wires leading to the pitot cannon plug were burned and broken. The pitot heat cannon plug and transducer cannon plug were burned. UHF, ILS, DC power and NR 3 fuel boost pump circuit breakers were popped. Power supplies for VOR and UHF were burned."

Not to show favoritism to jets alone, the Air Force gives this eyewitness account of a DC-3 encounter with a thunderstorm.

"At a point in the vicinity of Sutton, West Virginia, at about 0750E, a severe updraft was encountered which brought the nose up to the vertical position in spite of full forward pressure on the yoke. The plane continued on over until it was on its back, at which time the yoke was pulled to full backward position to recover. For the next 20 seconds normal flight was maintained at 3000 feet, but again a severe updraft was encountered and a loop was again made, recovering at 3000 feet. Following this the aircraft was rolled over on its back and a half loop was made, then it was thrown on its left side and at 1500 feet MSL the ground was sighted, only about 200 feet below the aircraft. Some altitude was gained but another loop occurred and the aircraft broke out of the overcast in a vertical dive with an air speed of around 240 miles per hour. It required strenuous efforts on the part of the crew to avoid striking the ground. Following this, conditions were again normal and the flight continued to Charleston and landed."

The final demonstration of thunderstorm activity on military aircraft is dramatically contained in one short item concerning the last moments of a giant KC-135, the jet tanker version of the Boeing 707. Powered by four jet engines, the KC-135 operates at speeds above 600 mph at altitudes over 50,000 feet. The plane has greatly increased the striking power of the Strategic Air Command by its ability to deliver full loads of fuel to jet bombers while on course and operating at operational jet speeds and altitudes. The report is brief:

"On a night mission the aircraft was flown into a thunderstorm at 41,200 feet. Control was lost due to severe turbulence, and structural limitations were exceeded. Primary structural failure occurred in the Nr 3 and Nr 4 engine strut attach points. This was followed by inflight disintegration of the aircraft. Primary cause was attributed to the pilot's entering clouds in the vicinity of known, avoidable thunderstorms."

The Air Force concludes the article on thunderstorms with eleven suggestions to pilots before taking off and while flying in the vicinity of thunderstorms, and the final reminder: "And once more, the one safe thunderstorm flight rule: DON'T."

Index